Cow
SIGNALS®

Udder Health

A practical guide to first-rate udder health

Authors:
Jan Hulsen, Vetvice
Theo Lam, UGCN

Content editing
Prof. Laura Green, University of Warwick

Translator
Sue Stewart, Stewart Translations

Photography
Jan Hulsen (unless stated otherwise)
Janneke Hulsen (p. 31, 35)
Otlis Sampimon (p. 20, 38, 39, 50)

Graphics
Marleen Felius
Emjee | graphic design
Verbaal, bureau for visual communication

Design and layout
Emjee | graphic design

Cover & layout English edition
Erik de Bruin, Varwig Design

ISBN 97890 8740 014 9
NUR 940

Vetvice®
Moerstraatsebaan 115
4614 PC Bergen op Zoom
Telephone: 00 31 (0)165 30 43 05
Fax: 0031 (0) 165 30 37 58
www.vetvice.com
info@vetvice.com

Roodbont Publishers
P.O. Box 4103
7200 BC Zutphen
Telephone: 00 31 (0) 575 54 56 88
Fax: 00 31 (0) 575 54 69 90
www.roodbont.com
info@roodbont.nl

UGCN
Dutch Udder Health Center
P.O. Box 2030
7420 AA Deventer
Telephone: 0900-7100071
www.ugcn.nl
info@ugcn.nl

With the participation of:
Hans Miltenburg (GD)
Otlis Sampimon (GD)
Quality Milk Production Services (NY, USA)

Udder Health is part of the *Cow Signals* series, which also includes *Cow Signals, Hooves* and *From calf to heifer.* Information about *Cow Signals* books, lectures and training courses can be found at: www.cowsignals.com.

And thanks to:
Johan Boelrijk, Tiny Brouwers, Joep Driessen, Marcel Drint, John Hermans, Ria Huijben, Paul Hulsen, Frans Kennis, Wim and Berrie van Kollenburg, Dick de Lange, Toon Meesters, Jo Toenders, Jos Uiterwaal, Jansje van Veersen, Nico Vreebrug, Bertjan Westerlaan, Ellen Wilpshaar and the many cattle farmers who kindly allowed us to take photographs on their farms. Not forgetting all of the farmers, vets and advisors who shared their knowledge and experience with us.

Contents

Mastitis or udder inflammation

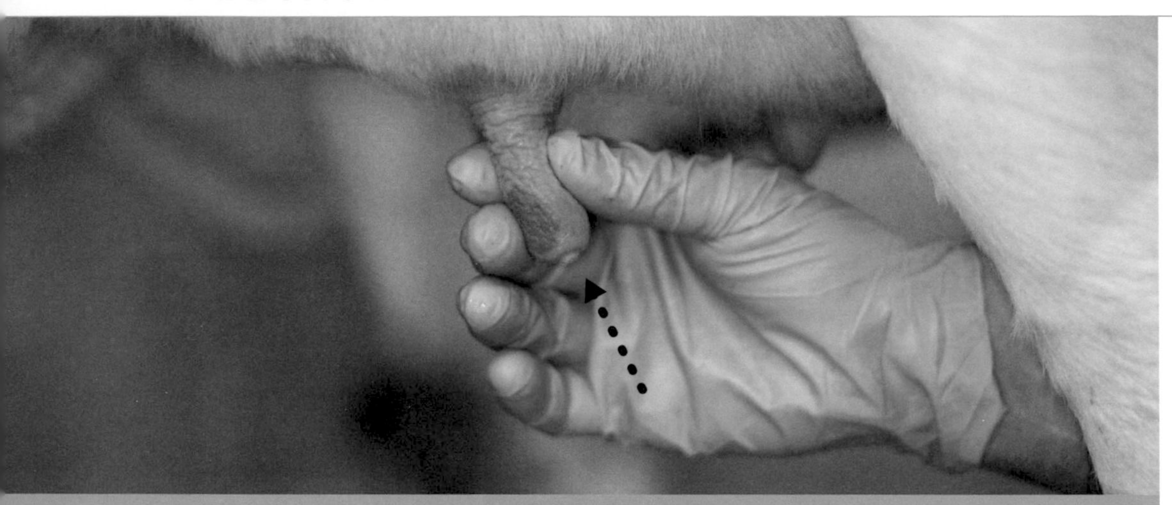

In almost every case, the organisms that cause mastitis enter the udder via the teat opening. This is why a strong immune system and excellent hygiene around the teat end are so vital in ensuring udder health.

Mastitis is caused by bacteria triggering an inflammatory reaction in the udder. The teat opening is supposed to keep bacteria out, and usually succeeds. Disinfecting the teat end with teat dip can help. But if the teat opening is not sealed, bacteria can sometimes get into the udder, for example during and after milking and at the start and end of the dry period. Most of these bacteria are flushed out again during milking, or are quietly dealt with by the immune cells in the udder. But if the immune response is too weak or the bacteria too strong or numerous, inflammation will occur.

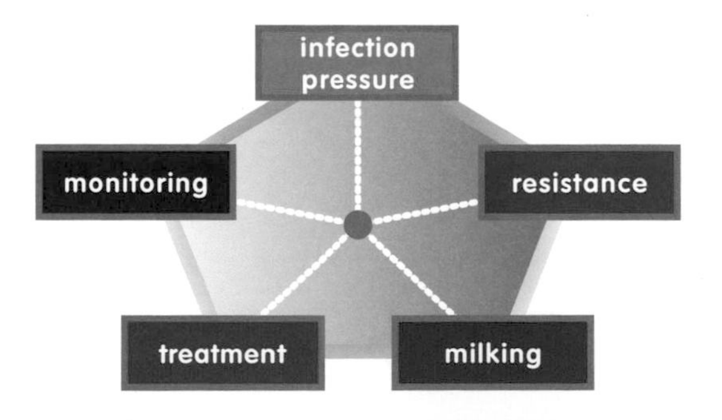

Our five-point plan

The udder health management on a dairy farm can be divided into five areas. Your job is to get each area under control as far as possible, and to keep it that way.

Crucial concepts

Infection and inflammation:
An infection is an invasion by disease-causing organisms. Inflammation is the body's immune response to foreign substances and objects such as bacteria.

Subclinical mastitis:
There are no visible signs of disease or infection in the milk or udder. The immune system mounts a mild response to an udder infection by sending more cells to the udder. Special techniques can be used to detect these changes such as cell counting and milk conductivity tests.

Clinical mastitis:
Visible inflammation by changes in the milk, and swelling and pain of the udder. The immune response is strong. The body temperature may rise and in some cases the cow becomes sick.

Types of mastitis bacteria

Contagious bacteria:
Bacteria transmitted from cow to cow via milk (milk-borne).

Environmental bacteria:
Bacteria entering the udder from the environment.

Management problem:

You have too much clinical and subclinical mastitis on your farm (cell count over 250,000). What do you do?

1. Identify all the problem cows and decide whether to treat or cull each animal. Problem cows have an elevated cell count and/or repeated occurrences of mastitis. Give each cow the most appropriate treatment, based on the farm treatment plan and bacteriological testing.

2. Make sure all areas of our five-point plan are under control, to prevent new cases of mastitis. Invest additional effort in the short term in order to stop infection from spreading from problem cows to healthy cows.

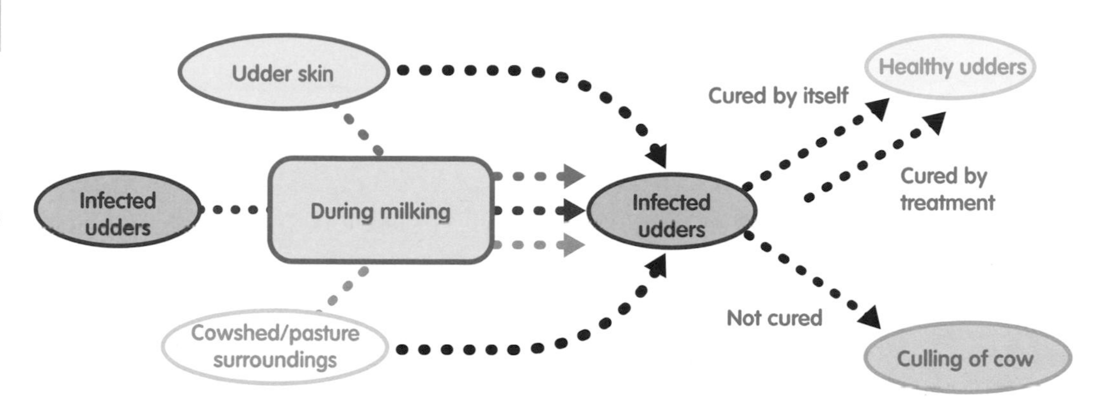

To prevent mastitis, you need to minimise the number of bacteria entering the udder. Clean and technically proficient milking and a clean farm are the key approaches.

Cows with mastitis may infect other cows. Isolate these animals and treat them as quickly as possible. Their surroundings should be clean and the resistance of cows and their udders should be as high as possible.

Cell count

The cell count is the number of cells per millilitre of milk. Milk always contains a certain number of cells: white blood cells responsible for immune defence, plus cells shed from the inner surfaces of the udder. In a healthy udder the cell count is below 100,000. When mastitis occurs, it is predominantly the number of white blood cells in the milk that rises.

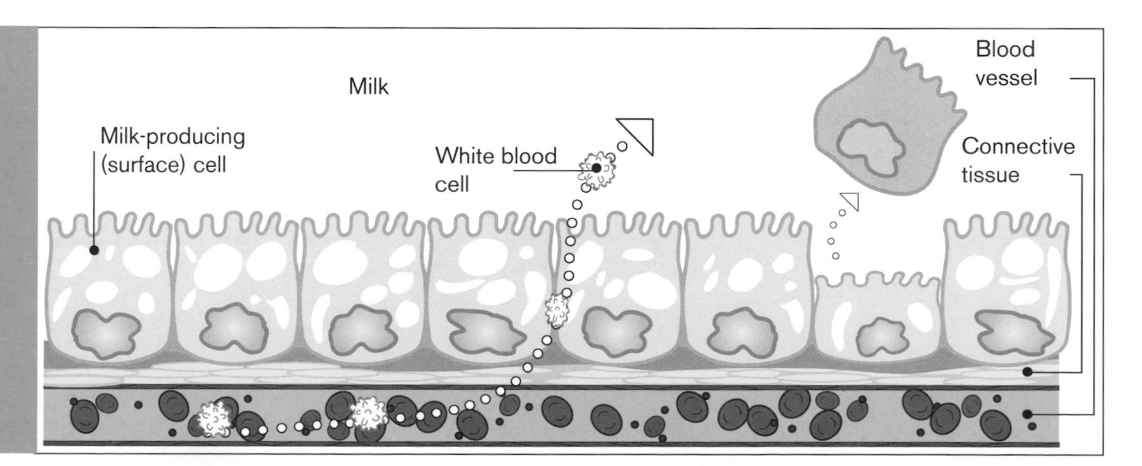

Structure and function of the udder

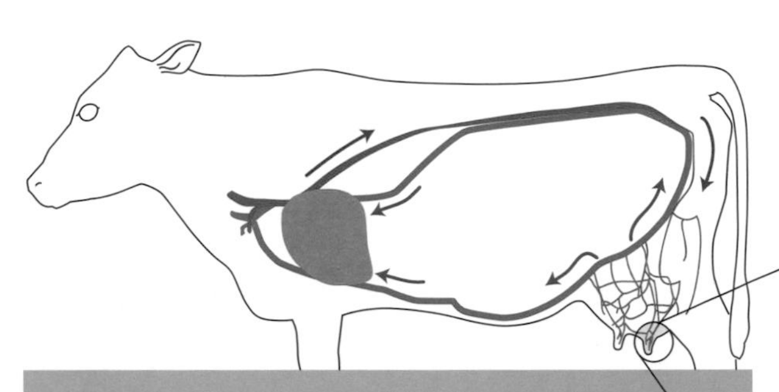

The two milk veins carry blood away from the udder to the heart. Two arteries supply blood to the udder, the cow is lying down, up to 20% more blood flows through the udder. For every litre of milk produced, approximately 500 litres of blood pass through the udder.

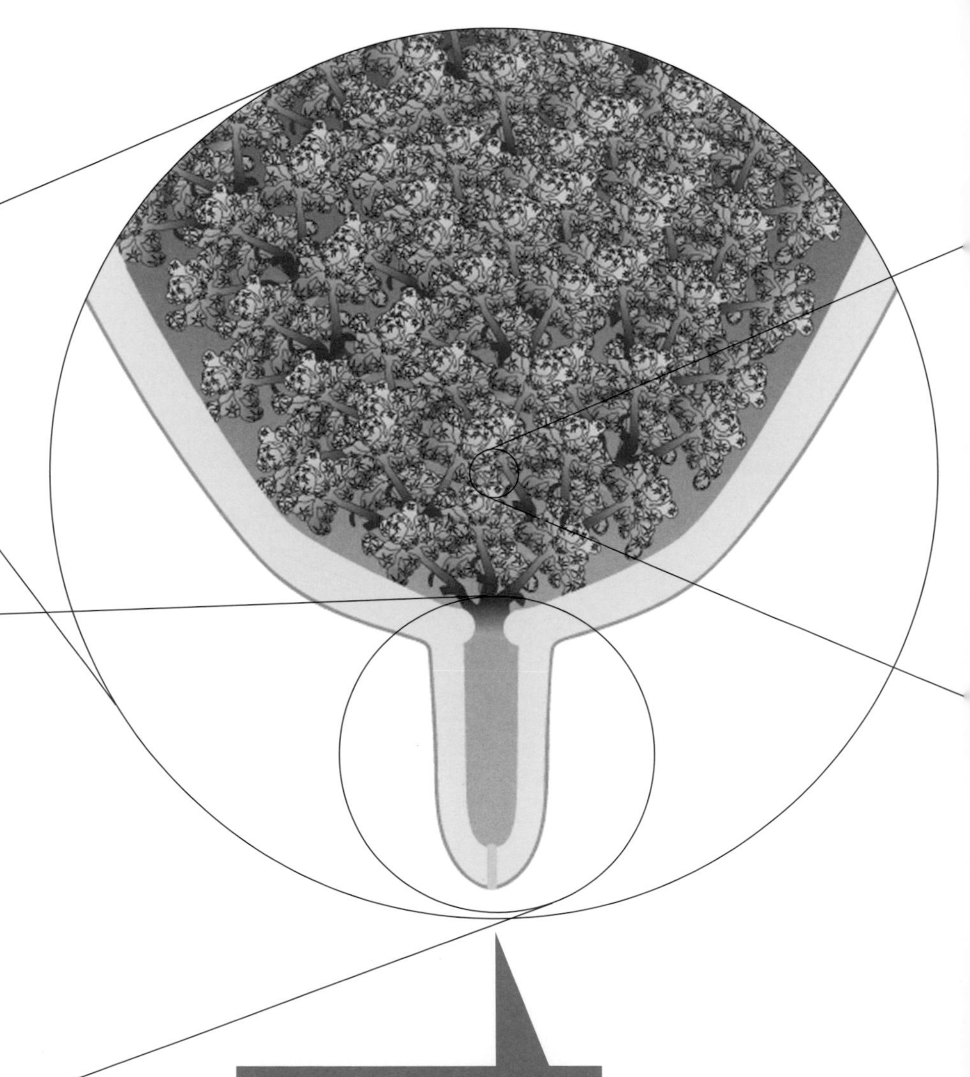

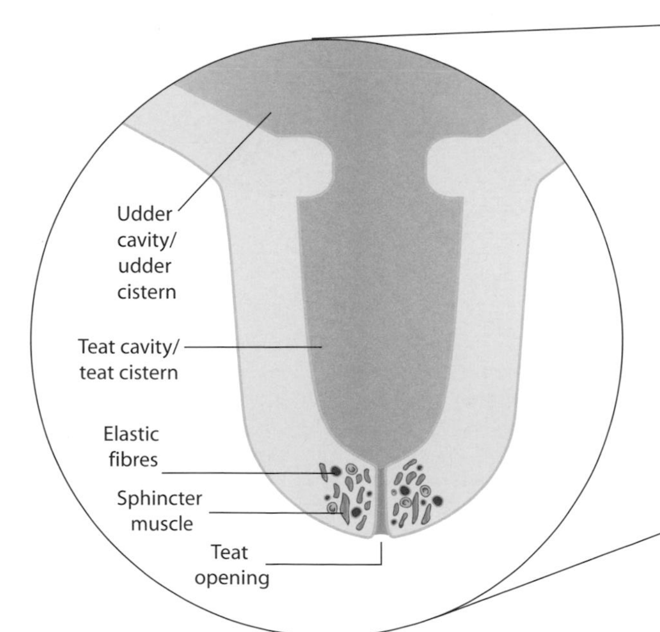

The teat and udder cisterns contain a small amount of free milk; the rest is stored in the alveoli. It is released when the cow lets the milk down.

Structure and function of the udder

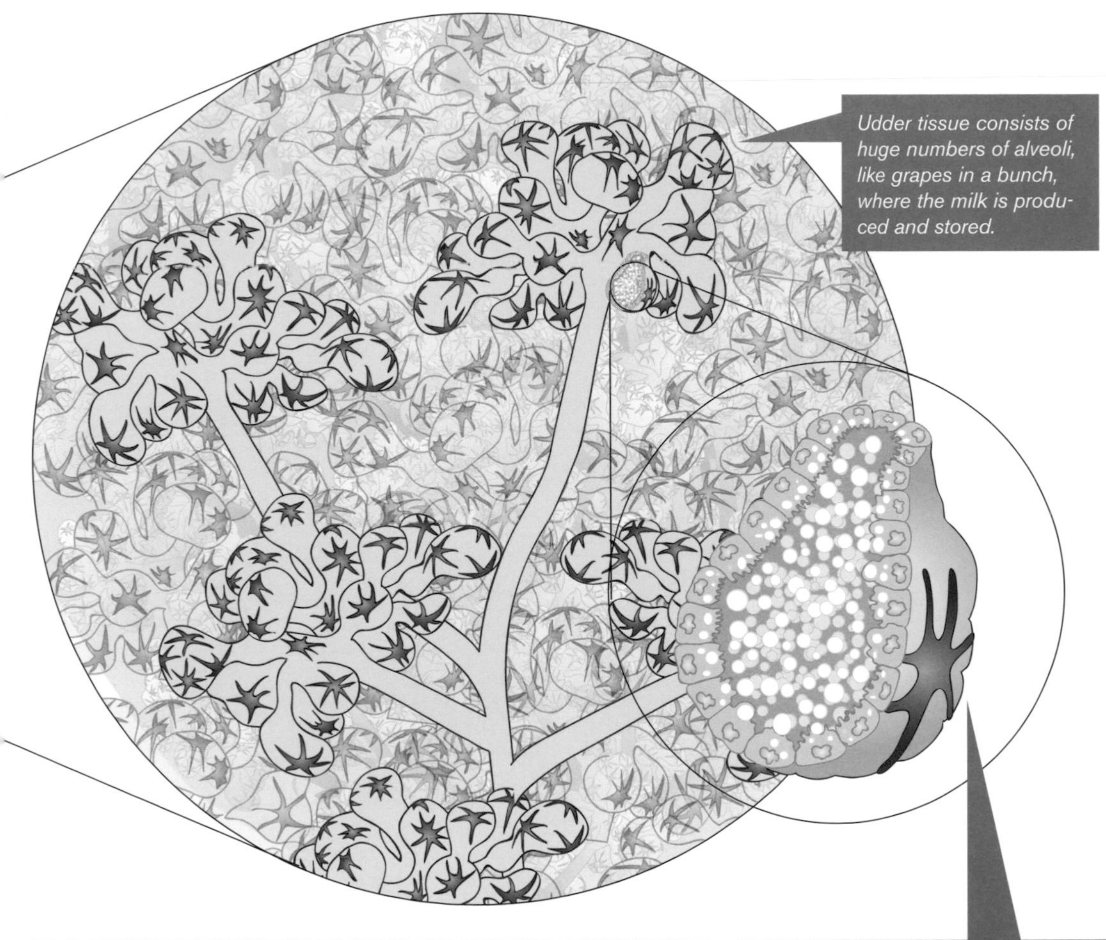

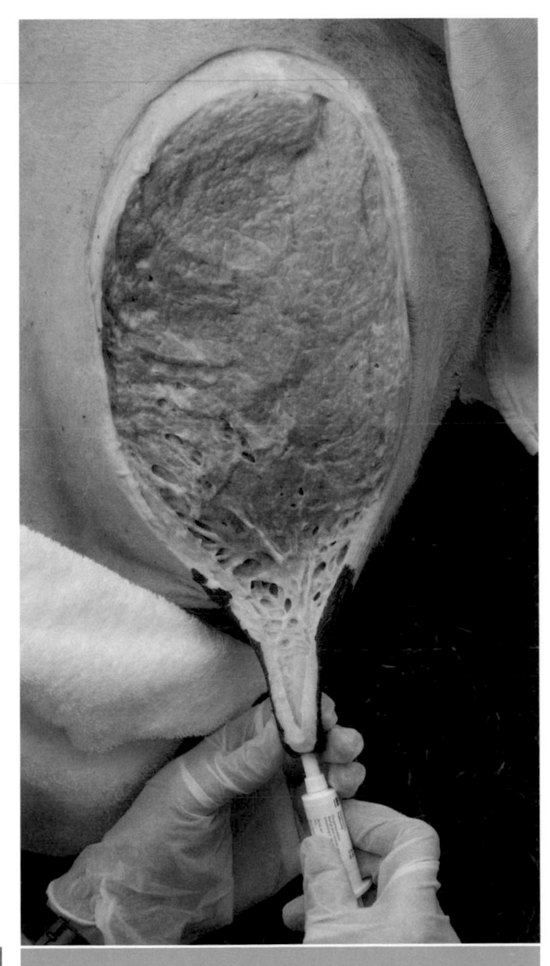

The teat canal is normally sealed with keratin, a paste-like substance produced by the surface cells of the teat canal.

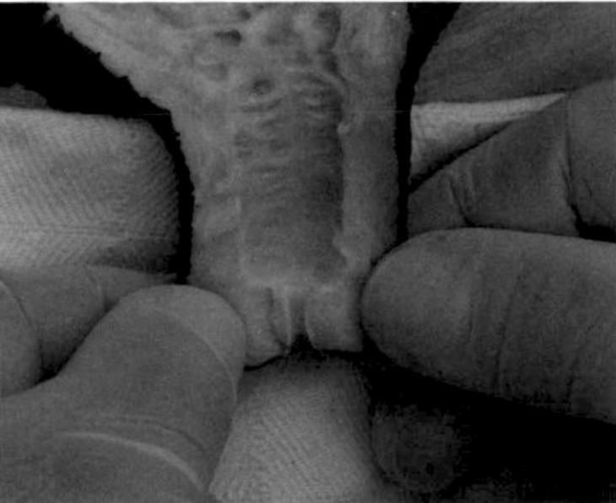

The small red stars are muscle cells. The hormone oxytocin causes them to contract, forcing the milk out of the alveoli towards the udder cistern and teat. This is milk let-down. Stimulation of the teat and teat end causes the brain to release oxytocin into the bloodstream. Agitation in the cow inhibits this process.

This is what the inside of an udder actually looks like. In a mastitic udder, the milk canals can become blocked by flakes or clots of milk and by swelling of udder tissue. An oxytocin injection can help milk out the cow. Concurrent treatment with antibiotics by injection plus intramammary tube gives a better result.

Udder health is something you work on every day. Some of this is obvious, such as treatments and cleaning cubicles. However, to some extent, udder health depends on general factors such as nutrition, rest and overall health.

Infection pressure is a combination of the number of organisms attacking the udder, and their virulence (strength). You really do not want them in your cows if you can avoid it. The ease with which organisms cause mastitis depends on the general health and resistance of the cow.

Low infection pressure of surroundings

Some environmental bacteria are always present, such as E. coli and S. uberis. These can be controlled by having dry cubicles, clean bedding and clean outdoor conditions, especially for dry cows. Others occur in certain conditions, for example, Klebsiella is usually present in wet sawdust, and Pseudomonas in contaminated water, teat dip or teat cloths.

Contagious bacteria:
bacteria transmitted from cow to cow via milk (milk-borne).
Environmental bacteria:
bacteria entering the udder from the environment.

The main mastitis-causing bacteria are always present on cows or in the cowshed or field, so trying to stop bacteria getting into the teat opening is a full-time job.

Infection pressure from cows

Cows with bacteria in their udders usually have raised cell counts and can cause new cases of mastitis in other cows. Infection between cows usually occurs during milking, which is why it is vital to milk hygienically and to identify cows with mastitis straight away. This will enable you to stop them passing on bacteria. These cows also pose a risk in the cowshed. Flies and milk leakage in cubicles can pass on the bacteria.

When cows huddle together, often the risk of mastitis increases due to higher infection pressure. Cows huddle when under stress; here, they are seeking shelter from the heat of the sun. They are stressed and their general resistance drops accordingly.

Good general resistance

A major cornerstone of resistance is optimal good feed and water intake. Cow nutrition is mainly about energy, protein and avoiding rumen acidosis. After that, minerals, vitamins and trace elements are important.
Resistance also depends on optimum rest and activity. A healthy cow in a well-run cowshed lies down for an average of 14 hours a day in a dry cubicle. Movement stimulates metabolism and hoof health.
In the end, the healthier the cow, the greater her resistance. Hoof problems and infectious diseases such as BVD and paratuberculosis (Johne's disease) reduce a cow's resistance to other diseases. The same is also true for all types of inflammation.

All cows must eat well throughout the day, maintaining a full rumen. Here are a lot of thin cows, cows with empty rumens and soiling due to watery dung. They are not eating enough and are probably selecting their feed. Their resistance to disease will be reduced.

Milk cows with mastitis and high cell counts last

You decide to start milking the cows with mastitis and a raised cell count at the end of each milking. This way all the cows needing treatment are together in the milking parlour at the same time. And you do not run the risk of passing on udder infections from infected to healthy cows. How do you go about this?

In practice, there are two solutions:

1. Mark with a leg band and separate out before milking.
This farmer has marked his cows with a neck band that he uses to separate them out quickly.

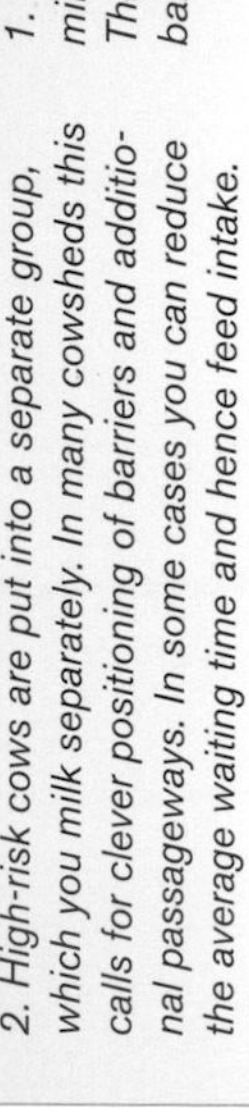

2. High-risk cows are put into a separate group, which you milk separately. In many cowsheds this calls for clever positioning of barriers and additional passageways. In some cases you can reduce the average waiting time and hence feed intake.

Once every four weeks, after assessing the cell count result from the milk recording results, determine which cows are high-risk and which are no longer high-risk.

Driving to the collecting yard

Cows should enter the milking parlour as peacefully as possible. This process starts with driving to the collecting yard before milking. At this point it is easy to see how well the cows are walking and their rumen fill tells you how much they have eaten in recent hours. The stragglers are particularly interesting, because these are usually the cows that are having difficulty walking. Have they eaten enough? Is their dung too watery, too dry or poorly digested? The collecting yard should also be an oasis of calm. At each milking, cows should have at most an hour's waiting time with twice-daily milking, and at most 45 minutes with three times per day milking.

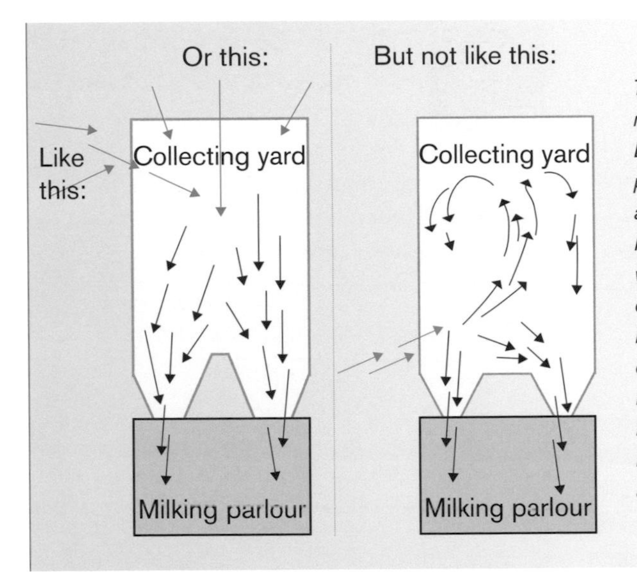

The cows should flow smoothly towards the milking parlour and should not have to turn. Dominant and low-status cows have distinct positions in a herd on the move, which helps to avoid conflict. The strongest cows often take the lead. If the cows have to turn both strong and weak animals have to cut across the flow. This causes agitation and stress, and an increase in hoof problems due to pushing and turning and entry to the milking parlour is disrupted. Rubber flooring also ensures cows sustain fewer hoof injuries from pushing and turning and are happy to enter the collecting yard but is not a alternative to good cow flow.

Peaceful and predictable handling is essential when dealing with cows. Calm farmers have cows that produce more milk. They are also much easier to handle and suffer fewer injuries. Calm cows are less likely to bump into and injure themselves on barriers or corners in the cow shed.

If cows have far to walk, their hooves are at greater risk of wear and damage, particularly on concrete paths and rough tracks with loose stones. Careful floor maintenance may help reduce sole ulcers and white line disease lameness. Cows prefer to walk on a soft surface with good grip, such as this rubber mat.

A collecting yard that slopes away from the parlour is easier to wash clean than a flat one. The entrances to the milking parlour should taper inwards. The floor of the milking parlour should be even to prevent hoof damage and should provide good grip.

Fresh, dry and cool

Fresh air without draughts helps to keep cows healthy and dry surroundings lower the concentration of bacteria in a building. Lactating cows generate a lot of heat. Cows feel comfortable between −5 and +15 °C. Any colder, and they start to use energy to warm themselves up. Any warmer, and they have to work to cool themselves down.

Heat stress reduces resistance.

Depending on the humidity in the cowshed, heat stress occurs above a temperature of 20 to 23°C, the point at which the maximum cooling capacity of the cow's airways is reached. At and above this point, the cows need help from fans to blow air over them, both in their cubicles and at the feed barrier.

Cooling

Cows cool themselves mainly via their breathing, but also via their skin. The air breathed in cools the airways, and the cow secretes water through her airways: in a sense, she sweats through her lungs. A cow radiates heat through her skin. Sweating helps to cool her down via the skin, but cows have limited sweating capacity. In still weather and in cowsheds with poor natural ventilation, fans can improve air quality in the shed even at lower temperatures. As a bonus, they make the shed drier. An insulated shed is cooler in summer and warmer in winter.

In the cowshed

All cows should have access to water at all times and should be offered tasty food of the correct composition. Have you got this right for your herd?

Things to check in your shed:

Do your cows start to eat straight away, or do they search about and dawdle?

Are you collecting 5% or more left-over feed every day?

Is the composition of left-over feed and the original diet the same?

Do all dry cows, heifers, lame cows and newly calved cows eat enough thoughout the day (rumen fill always over 3)?

Does the shed or field have at least one fast-flow drinking trough to every 15 cows, or one reservoir-type trough to every 20 cows, evenly spaced and containing clean water?

A yes to all these is good.

For more information see another book in this series: Cow Signals.

Having open sides, insulating the roof, grooving floors or laying rubber and installing fans are things that can be done in every cowshed. Wide paths ensure that food and water are accessible and that cows can be driven smoothly and calmly to the collecting yard. Hoof problems make cows walk less, lie down less, eat less and drink less.

Hygiene score

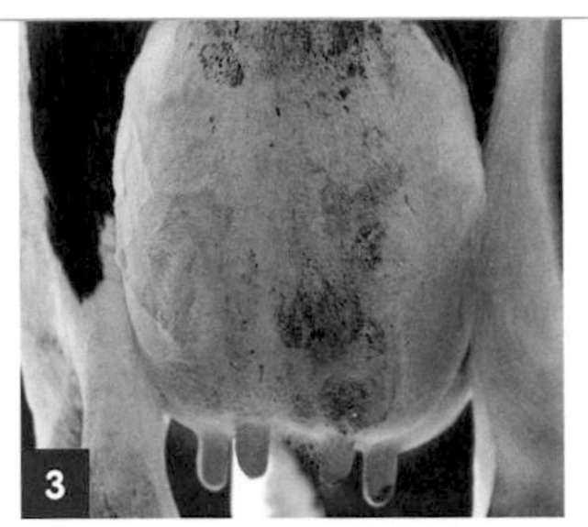

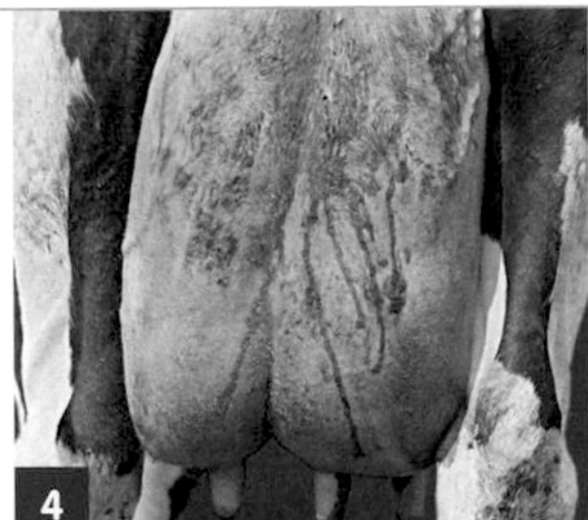

rear view of udder

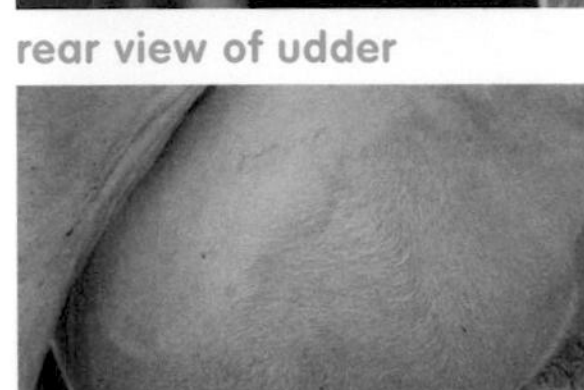

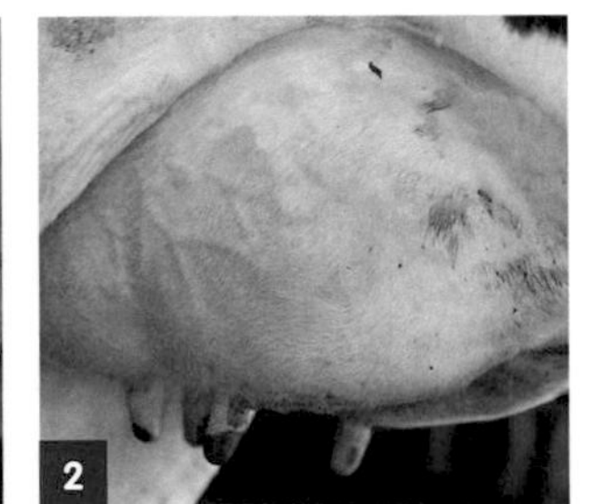

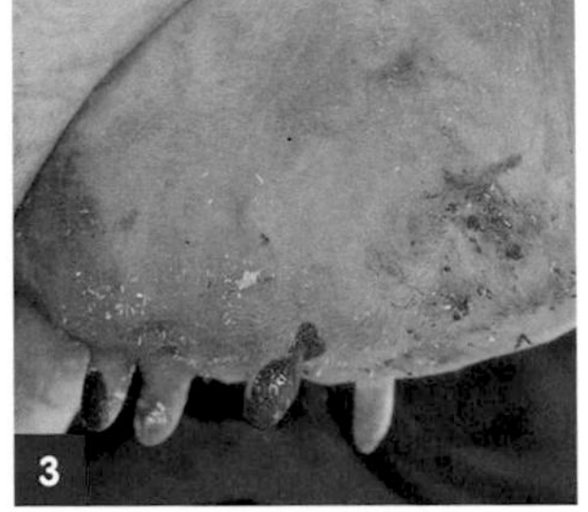

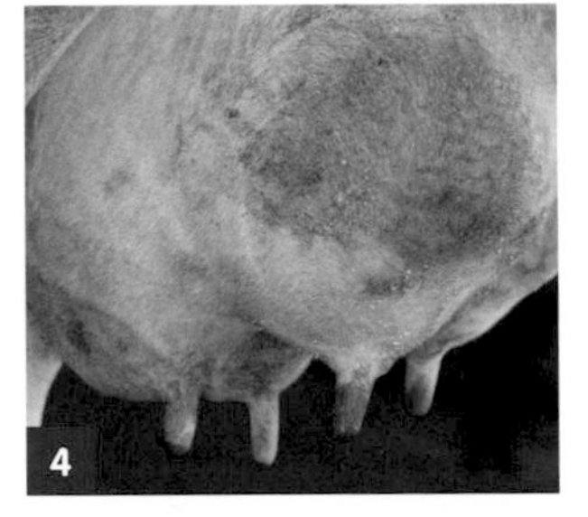

side view of udder

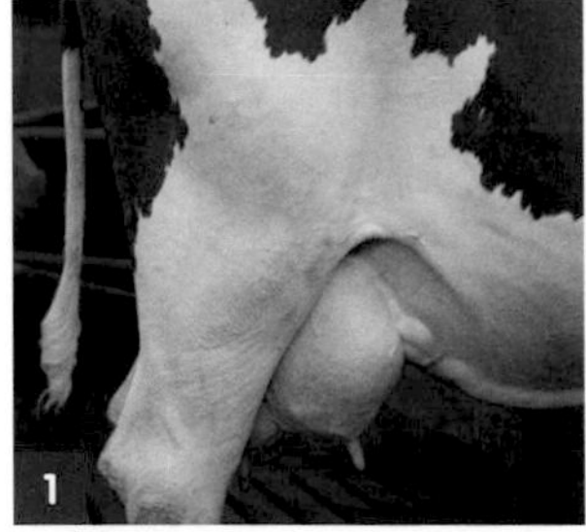

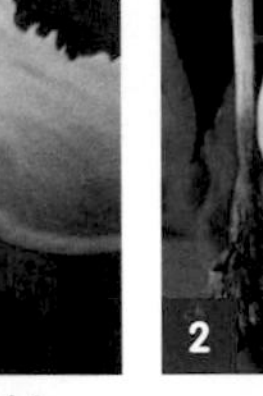

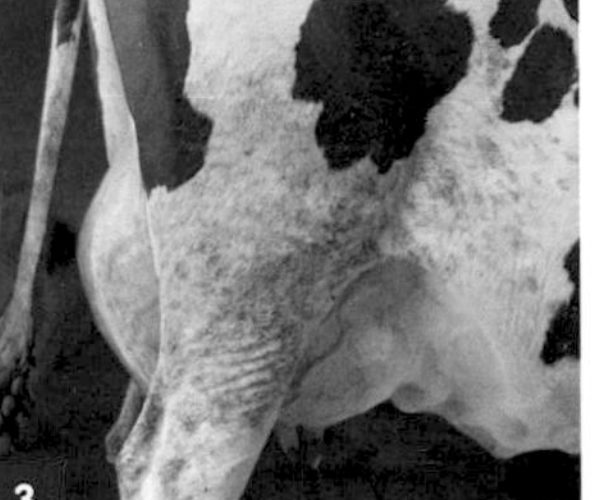

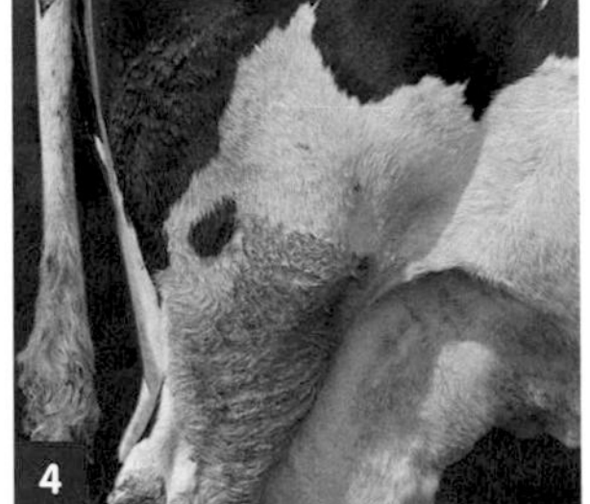

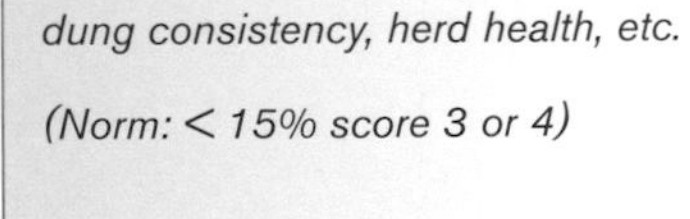

side view of rump and hip

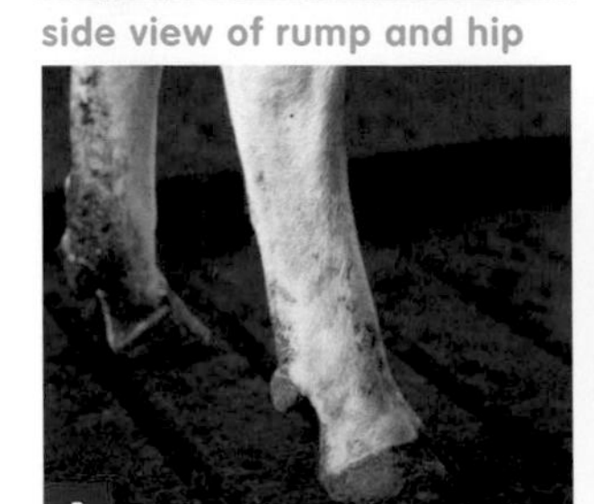

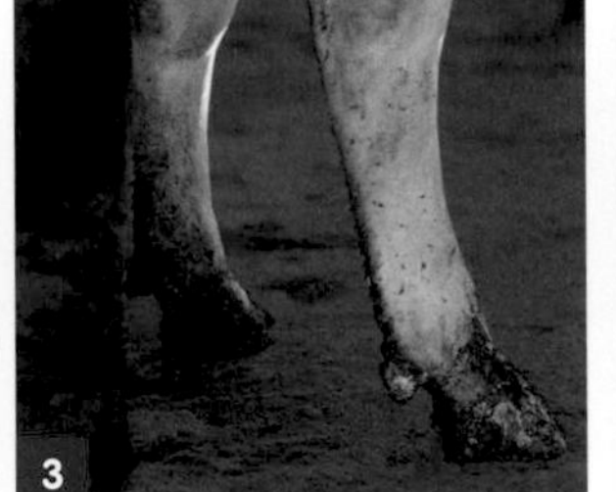

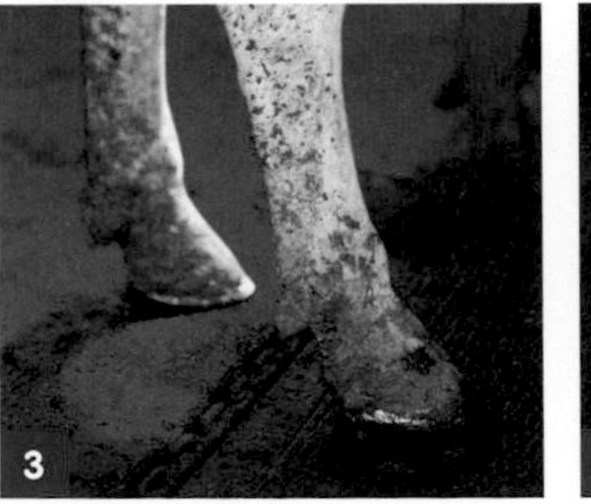

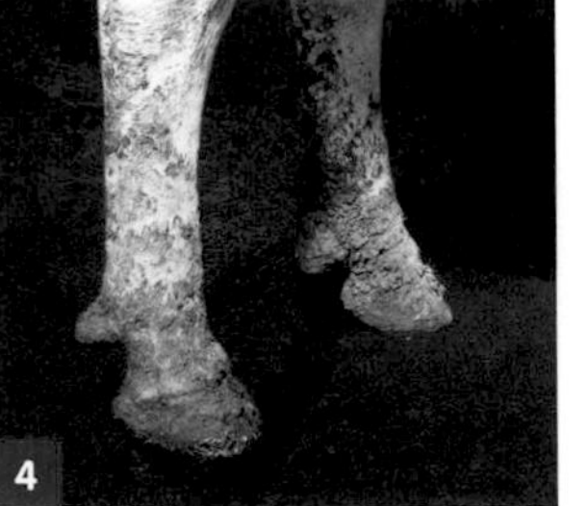

side view of hind legs and hooves

Factors that influence scores

Udder hygiene:
How clean are udders and teats on entry to the milking parlour?

Points to watch: hygiene and bedding in lying areas, path hygiene, udder clipping or singeing, cubicle comfort, dung consistency, herd health, etc.

(Norm: < 10% score 3 or 4)

Upper leg hygiene:
How clean are the lying areas?

Points to watch: preparation of lying areas and bedding, cubicle comfort, dung consistency, herd health, etc.

(Norm: < 15% score 3 or 4)

Lower leg and hoof hygiene:
How clean are the paths?

Points to watch: use of dung scraper, cleanliness of paths not cleared by dung scraper, dung consistency, cleanliness of collecting yard, etc.

(Norm: < 20% score 3 or 4)

Hygiene of cows and their surroundings

Cows should be clean

Clean cows have clean teats and are healthier. Soiling indicates that the cow's surroundings are too wet or contanimated with dung, and hence a cows' resistance is under constant pressure. Dirty cows are a sign that their dung is too watery or that they are having trouble standing up before defecating. This tells you that their nutrition, health and cubicles could be improved. Finally, soiling is a sign that the farmer is accepting his animals' less-than-ideal situation too readily.

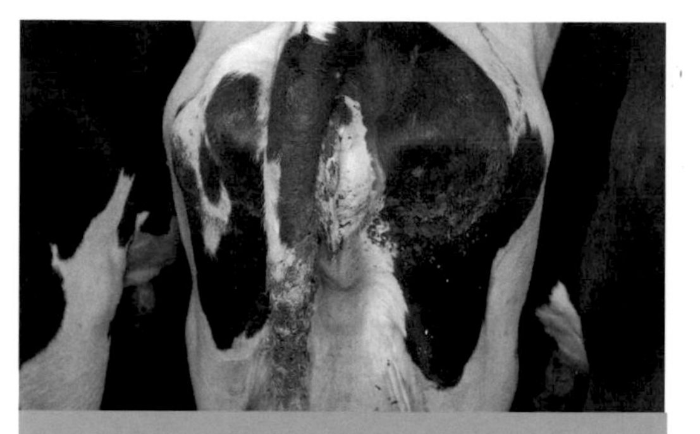

A discharge due to metritis soils the tail and causes streaks on the rump. Metritis may be a sign that the transition from dry period to lactation did not go well. Affected cows are more susceptible to mastitis.

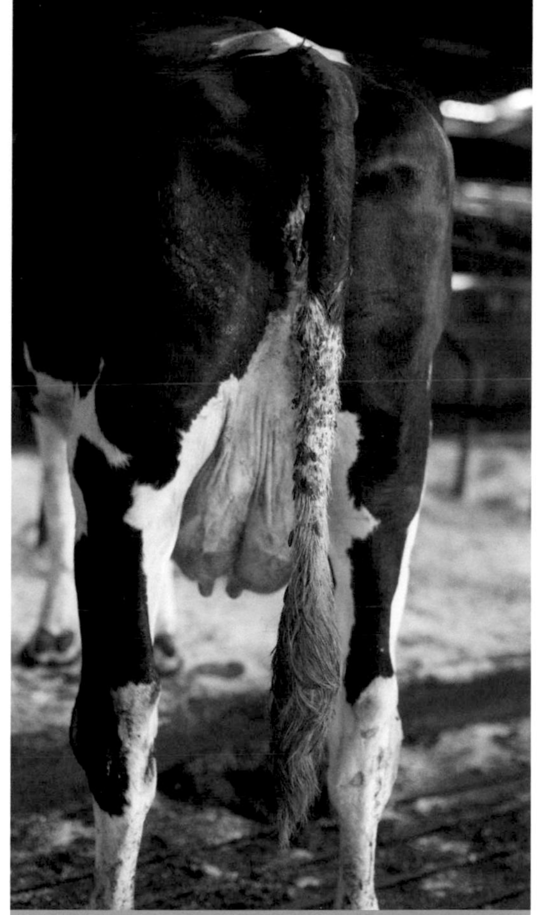

A dirty tail and soiled hindquarters are almost always due to watery dung of the cow herself. Cubicles that are too short and a wet floor can make this problem worse. Tail clipping promotes udder hygiene.

How hygienically do you work?

Ask your family, friends and colleagues the following questions:

1. *Do you know how cleanly I work when milking, assisting calvings and looking after newborn calves?*
2. *Am I sometimes too quick to assume that "it'll turn out all right" when I have a cow with clots in her milk or a high cell count, or a cow calving in a dirty calving pen?*
3. *Do I ensure excellent hygiene in cubicles, dry cows, calving cows and during milking?*
4. *Do you think I take criticism on board and try to improve myself?*

Know yourself, because you, the farmer, are the most important influence on health and production of your herd. You should be constantly checking that you are working cleanly and correctly and achieving top quality results every day in terms of the nutrition and health of your cows. You may need to take more trouble over some things, do other things differently, get someone else to take on some of the tasks, or not do some things at all.

Comfortable cubicles

Adequate rest stimulates cows' resistance. If their cubicles are comfortable enough, cows will lie for 14 hours a day. It also gives hooves a chance to dry, which suppresses infections. Resting cows are out of the way, giving other cows more space to get to feed, water, brushes, milking robots or cubicles. If there is at least one comfortable cubicle available per cow, weaker and low-status animals will have fewer problems with feed intake, water intake and lameness (provided that good, tasty feed is available at all times).

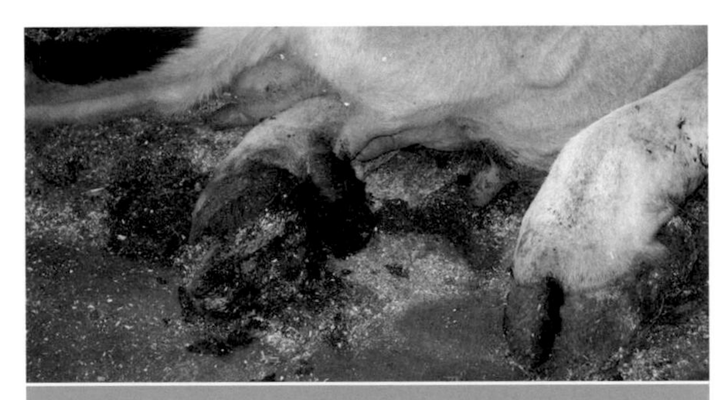

While a cow is lying down, her teats are resting on her hooves or on the floor. This means that hooves and cubicle floors should always be as clean and dry as possible. All cubicles should be cleaned thoroughly twice a day (ideally during milking). They should also be freshened up twice a day (during your rounds). Top up the bedding daily.

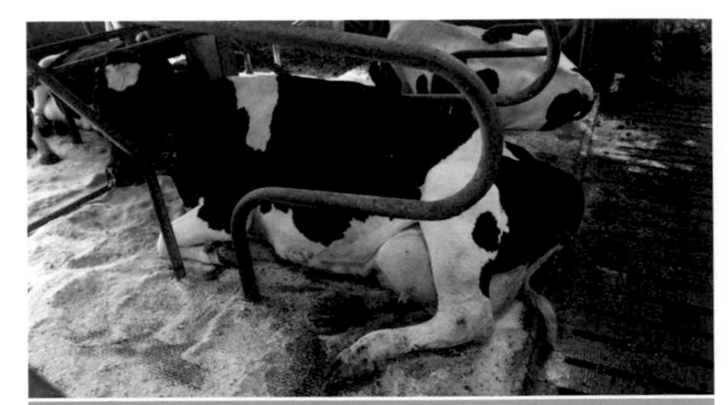

Milk leakage poses a risk for infection. Variable intervals between milkings and cows that milk out fast increase milk leakage. Inadequate calcium intake can also play a role. Leakage may be greater in comfortable cubicles than in hard, short or narrow ones. This is because cows tend to lie down more in them and their lying position may also have an effect. Put mattress cubicles on a 3 to 4% incline.

Bedding should be dry and free of mastitis organisms as far as possible. Try to mechanise the changing of bedding. Regular bacteriological testing of mastitis samples will tell you whether the bedding is causing udder infections.

Cubicle comfort points:	Friesian Holstein cow 725 kg:
1. soft floor providing good grip so the cow lands and lies softly:	≥15 cm deep bedding or ≥5 cm rubber mattress;
2. long enough, so the cow can swing her head out to rise easily:	outer row: ≥3.25 m, double row: ≥5.50 m together; headroom: no obstacles between a height of 0.10 and 1.00 m;
3. withers and knee bars out of the way, in correct position so the cow can stand up and lie down straight in the cubicle:	≥1.80m distance from knee bar and withers bar to back edge (standing/lying area); possibly install flexible withers band;
4. wide enough, so the cow can lie down and remain lying down:	1.27 m (heart to heart measurement);
5. used by strong cows with healthy legs:	Put poor cows in a straw-bedded pen.

To ensure comfortable cubicles, use the largest cows as your standard. After installation you can tailor the cubicles to your herd if necessary. Heifers are the smallest cattle and will soil cubicles most often. A separate heifer group with smaller cubicles will solve the problem and also improve production and reduce losses.

Before milking

An ideal time to inspect the cows is while walking to the parlour. Cows with mild lameness stand out. Animals that are not alert and animals with empty rumens are also noticeable.
Schedule time every day for individual inspection and treatment of animals that require attention. This will enable you to avoid many problems such as lameness and twisted stomachs. Problems are always unexpected, inconvenient and take up valuable time. If you mark newly calved cows you will automatically give them more attention.

Dry cows and heifers

Schedule two fixed rounds a day for dry cows and heifers. Combine these with jobs such as cubicle preparation. Here the dry cows' teat are being dipped.

Cows who know that fresh feed awaits them in the feed trough after milking will enter and exit the milking parlour more easily. Check and make sure all animals can drink freely after milking. Put the water trough near the milking parlour, but not so that cows drinking there block the exit.

After milking

After milking, ensure cows stand for at least 30 minutes once the last cow has been milked. During this time the teat openings seal up, reducing the risk of udder infection when they next go to lie down. This can be done by keeping the cows at the feed barrier for half an hour, or closing the cubicle house. Even the last cows to leave the milking parlour should eat first and not go straight to a cubicle. Cows that don't go to eat are a sign that something is wrong. Why are they lying down or skulking? Are they lame or sick? Or is there no space for them due to overcrowding or ranking order anxiety?

If cubicle floors are too smooth and/or too narrow, cows will 'scrabble' with their hind legs to gain a grip when standing up. One consequence of this is trapped teats. Agitation in the cubicle also increases the likelihood of trapped teats.

Good lighting (≥200 lux) lets you see everything clearly. Coloured light can make it difficult to tell the difference between urine, milk, blood, mucus and pus.

Administering veterinary medicines

Treatments call for an organised and calm approach.

Injection in the neck (intramuscular)

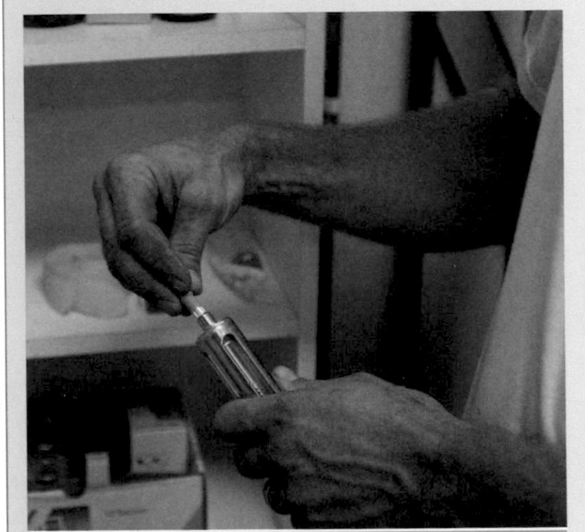

1. New needle.

2. Use 100% clean injection fluid.

3. Keep records.

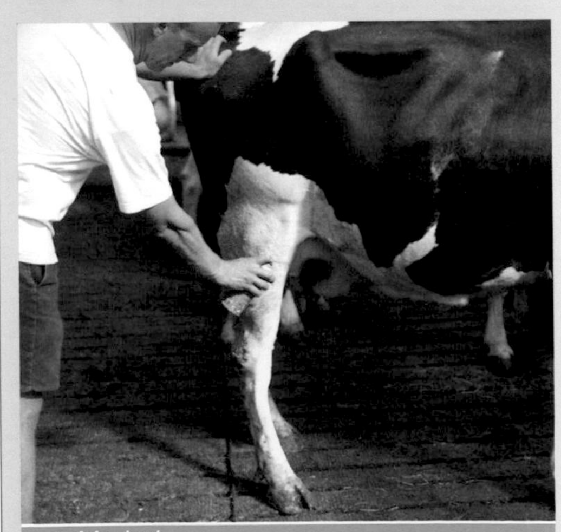

4. Mark the cow.

5. Cow stands nice and still.

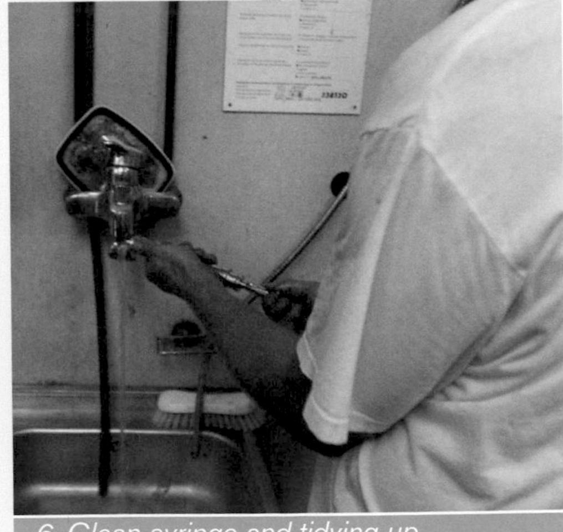

6. Clean syringe and tidying up.

Administering veterinary medicines

Finding the right injection site

Intramuscular (into the muscle)

Inject at right angles to the skin, in the green triangle. The triangle is a hand's width in front of the shoulder blade, under the neck edge and above the neck vertebrae (purple line).

Subcutaneous (under the skin)

Take a fold of skin and insert the needle diagonally between the skin and underlying muscles. Subcutaneous injections in the neck can be given in the triangle indicated above, as far as the pink line.

Inserting an intramammary tube

Choose a clean place where you can work in an organised manner, such as the milking parlour. Mark the cow. Start by cleaning the teats carefully. Intramammary tubes contain chemicals. Wear gloves and make sure no spilled tube contents get into the milking clusters or the milk!

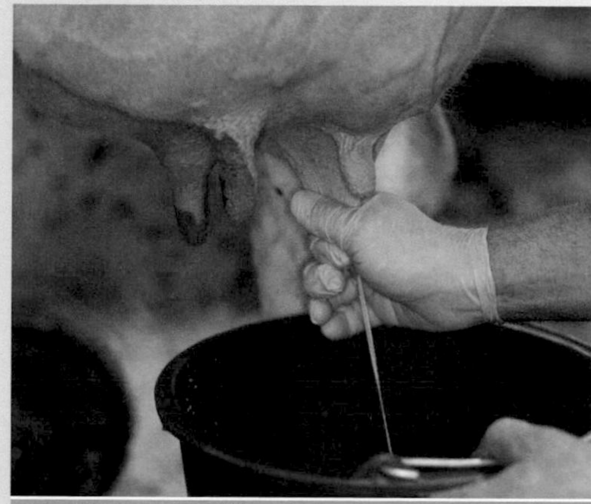

1. Strip foremilk.

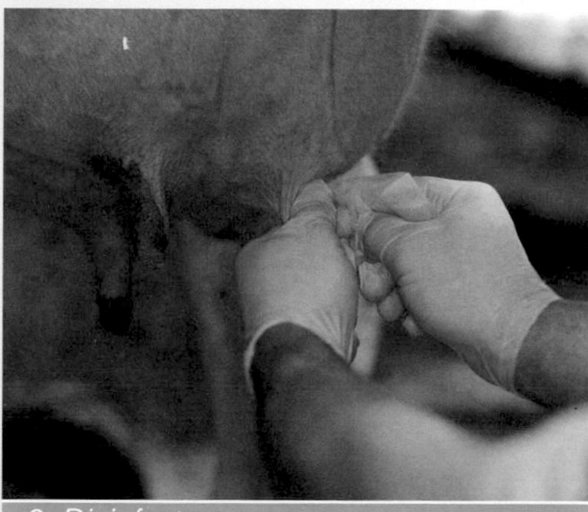

2. Disinfect.

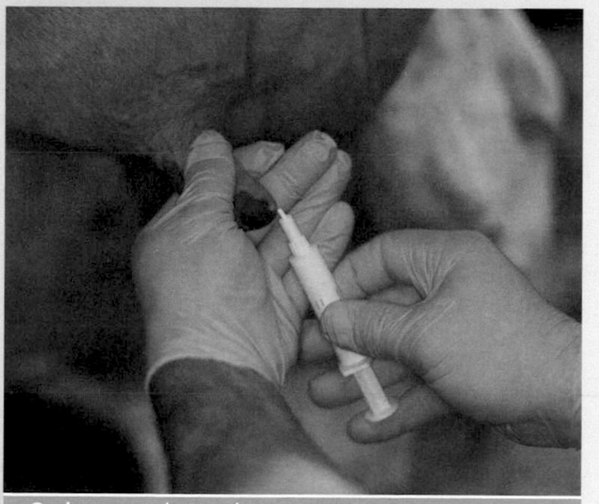

3. Insert short tip.

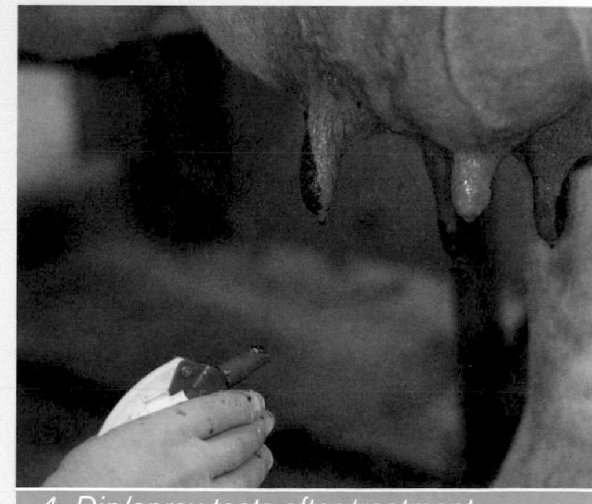

4. Dip/spray teats after treatment.

An intramammary tube widens the teat canal and pushes the keratin layer inside. Make sure your hygiene is impeccable when using tubes without antibiotics.

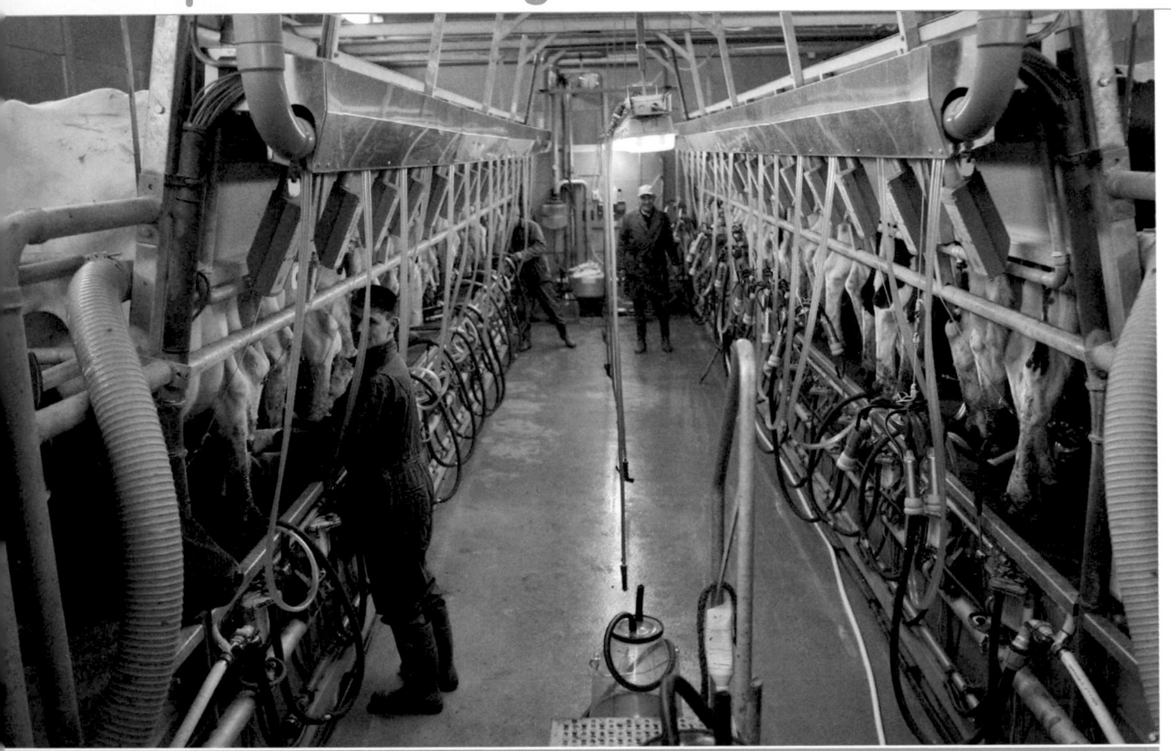

A pleasant workplace encourages you to work better. Make sure your parlour is comfortable and efficient. Think about ease of working, space and organisation, ventilation, temperature (including the floor), cleanliness, dryness, plenty of light and music.

The factors that determine the success of milking are a milking machine in first-rate working order, excellent milking technique, and clean and calm cows. 'Milking technique' means the accurate, hygienic completion of the following activities: foremilk stripping and pre-dipping, attaching the cluster, positioning the cluster, detaching the cluster and dipping/spraying.

Every cow is important

Milking may be a routine activity, but every cow must receive due attention. Every milker should know what to do and why, and the milking parlour should be a pleasant place to work. The good milker (you) knows every cow with a high cell count and spots every new case of mastitis. The farm treatment plan tells you what to do next.

Reducing high cell count

For years, many farms have been able to control their cell count, and milk-borne udder infections in particular, by paying careful attention to these five points.

1. milking technique and milking machine;
2. dipping teats properly;
3. treating mastitis;
4. drying off with antibiotics;
5. culling chronically infected cows.

This programme is incomplete, since it lacks good resistance of the cow as a success factor. And you still run the risk (although greatly reduced) of mastitis due to environmental bacteria. It remains necessary for all farms to maintain constant vigilance by means of cell count monitoring and bacteriological testing.

If you need glasses to read the newspaper, you need them for milking as well. You need to be able to see every tiny clot in the milk. And make sure you have enough light under the cow and near the teats (400 lux).

Entry and exit

The rate at which cows enter and exit the milking parlour influences her capacity and varies widely from farm to farm. Competent milkers in well-organised parlours rarely have to fetch cows in.

Cows must learn to come into the milking parlour calmly and quietly. This applies to new animals and to all cows if you have a new parlour. Cows are creatures of habit. Older cows are poor learners, while heifers learn quickly.

Cows must leave the milking parlour quickly and smoothly, otherwise they prolong the milking time. The milker will also be inclined to hurry them along, which causes agitation in the parlour. Bad experiences in the milking parlour disrupt the entry process.

Peaceful enticement

The only way to entice cows into the parlour is with tasty feed. Use fresh feed at the feed barrier as an enticement to get cows passing through the parlour smoothly. Concentrate feed in the parlour draws the cows in but often leads to agitation during milking: once it is finished the cows start to look for more food.

Healthy, calm animals enter a well-organised parlour without problems. However, a degree of persuasion may still be necessary, such as a moving barrier. But always make sure the animals remain calm and don't use the barrier to push them.

Let the gate make a warning sound when moving forward. Don't use electric shocks.

Cows in the collecting yard

These cows are in the collecting yard but are heading away from the parlour. Why is this?

Answer:

The animals are afraid of people or the milking parlour. They must be able to walk to their places confidently and unimpeded. This means space, grip, no obstacles and a peaceful atmosphere. The parlour should be fresh and airy.

Cows soon become anxious and overheated when close together. Fans cool them down, bring in fresh air and keep flies away. In the collecting yard, direct the flow of air lengthways and down towards the cows' heads. In the parlour, ventilate from the centre towards the cows.

Shouting and hitting produces timid animals that are difficult to handle. Calm, friendly, cow-oriented parlour workers milk faster and obtain more litres per cow. They talk to the cows and touch them frequently. Some cows get accustomed to being fetched and come to expect it.

Check the vacuum before milking. Stick a strip of tape at the right position, which will also be helpful for relief milkers. Has the milking machine been cleaned properly? Is there still enough oil in the vacuum pump reservoir?

Scheduled maintenance

A scheduled overhaul of the milking system once a year will assure that the equipment is in good condition. Follow the supplier's instructions. Arrange for the supplier to deliver new liners at the right time. Rubber liners should be replaced after 2,500 milkings on average (approximately every 8 months). Silicone liners often last twice as long. Some liners have to be withdrawn after 500 milkings. Old rubber loses its elasticity and puts more stress on the teats. The inside becomes porous, which makes it easier for bacteria to gain a foothold. Write the date you need to order new liners on the calendar.

A heating element gives you constant access to water over 80 °C, so you can rinse out the cluster after a high cell count cow. Many farms have a separate hot water tap in the milking parlour.

Checking the clusters

Replace perished tubes immediately. Air leaking in through a hole disrupts the vacuum.

Many liners have a mark on the lip and milk tube. These should be aligned to ensure that the liner is not twisted.

If the short milk tubes are twisted they twist the teat cup, so it no longer hangs directly beneath the teat.

Clever standard procedures

Ready for action

The milking process and milking parlour should be organised to maximise efficiency. Simple, sound procedures ensure that you and your staff always do your work properly. If you follow well thought-out and organised procedures you can do everything right the first time, with minimum trouble and expense.

The essentials

When you start to milk, the milking machine must be working properly. You should have all the relevant information about the cows. All the equipment should be ready for milking and available for use if necessary.

Example: dry pre-treatment

Each teat must be cleaned thoroughly with a clean cloth. The milker needs to massage the udder at the same time, so should have a good grip. This is possible with paper towels, but fabric is often better.

In the operator's pit you need separate baskets and bags for clean and dirty cloths. A washing machine in the parlour provides a ready supply of clean udder cloths and clean work clothes. Put a wash on after each milking, and make sure the previous wash is drying.

Getting into good habits

You will automatically start each milking with clean dip and a clean dip cup if you always empty and rinse out the dip cup after milking.

Thinking through your routines

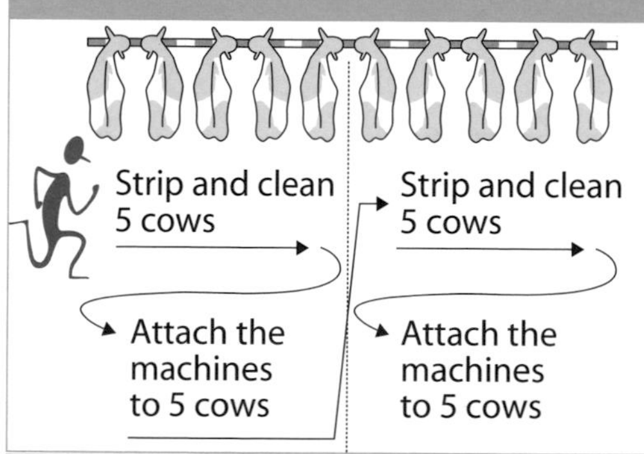

This farm has worked out the ideal milking routine and set it down in a useful diagram. They use it to keep each other on the ball. It is displayed in or near the operator's pit.

Having everything to hand

Dirty teats have to be washed and dried. This is easy if you have tepid running water to hand and a cloth for drying the teats properly. (Make sure you never have to wash more than 1 in 20 udders.)

Identifying infected cows

Identifying infected cows

Every cow with an increased cell count or evidence of mastitis should ring alarm bells with the milker. Animals like these pose a serious risk to other cows, and you need to make sure their udder infections are treated. Assess the condition of cows and udders at each milking, then treat in accordance with your farm treatment plan. The best procedure is to gather all the high cell count cows together and milk last at the end of milking. This ensures that treatment holds up milking as little as possible. It also eliminates the risk of udder infections spreading to healthy cows milked subsequently.

Rinsing the milking cluster

After milking cows with a high cell count, you should kill any bacteria in the cluster by disinfecting. If you don't, the next four to five cows could become infected with S. aureus for example. Bacteria can be killed by rinsing the liner with hot water. Immerse the liner for at least thirty seconds in water over 80 °C. At 85 °C all S. aureus are killed after five seconds. Tepid water containing disinfectant takes two minutes to work. Then flush out the cluster thoroughly, to wash out the disinfectant.

The filter should be clean after milking. If it's not, you know you haven't been working cleanly or have failed to notice a cow with clots in her milk.

Identifying and reacting

If the high cell count cows enter the parlour randomly, it is important to identify them immediately and to do what needs to be done with each animal. This is and always will be the job of the milker. A milker can remain fully alert for about an hour. After that, he or she will need to take a short break. The milking machine can help in identifying high-risk cows, e.g. by means of alarm lights and automatic milk separation.

- *lights (red-yellow-green)*
- *displays (showing the cow's number)*
- *leg bandages*

Any system is only as good as the commitment that goes into operating it. Commitment follows automatically when people know why they have to do things, can do their work easily and can see the results of their work (that is, knowledge, organisation and monitoring/analysis of outcomes).

Identifying abnormalities

Good treatment starts with early identification of abnormal milk and abnormal cows. Foremilk stripping is usually essential in order to detect abnormal milk. Whether to treat a cow and how to treat her are indicated in the farm treatment plan. The plan lists the signs that determine which treatment to administer. Display a copy in the milking parlour, and near the drugs cabinet. Only if you know which cows have abnormal milk can you specifically combat the transmission of infections, by rinsing out the milking cluster for example. All abnormal milk is waste. Only colostrum should be given to the calf.

If you have everything to hand and ready to use, you will use it. The following should be in or near the operator's pit:

- *a thermometer;*
- *equipment for carrying out a CMT;*
- *equipment for taking milk samples;*
- *drugs and equipment for treating mastitis;*
- *equipment for marking cows;*
- *a system for recording treatment and any unusual findings.*

The operator's pit is not a good place for giving injections, but it is OK for administering intramammary tubes.

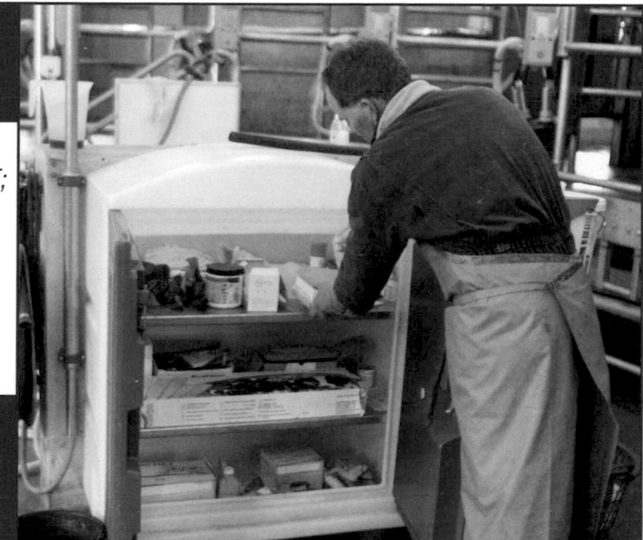

Doing it right

Do you know which of your cows need treatment, and do you make sure that others know as well?

Answer:

Milk and gather with focus, use and pass on cow-related information to other workers as part of your daily routine. You have four systems at your disposal:

1. *mark cows using a code system;*
2. *use codes via the display in the milking parlour (management system);*
3. *pass on information verbally, milker knows every cow;*
4. *use information on noticeboard/list, milker knows every cow.*

In practice, you work with several systems at the same time. For example, you mark cows, enter alerts in the management system and make notes on a noticeboard.

Milking procedure

Why we do this:		
Clean teats and teat openings mean a low risk of infection. If a teat is wet the teat cup rides up, putting greater stress on the teat.	Foremilk stripping helps to identify mastitis early. (Alternative: clot detector in milk tube). It also promotes the release of oxytocin, shortening milking times and improving milking out.	Attaching at the right time reduces the stress on the teat and shortens the milking time.
(Initial clean)	**1. Foremilk stripping and pre-treating** 	**2. Attaching the cluster**
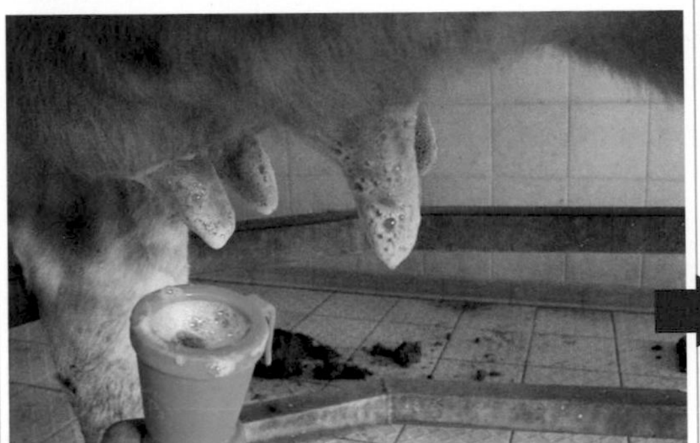		
– wash and dry very dirty teats; – if necessary, soften the teats with a pre-treatment agent.	– express three squirts of milk; – clean teat and teat end thoroughly and dry with a clean cloth; – massage teat and udder for at least 15 seconds; – keep hands clean	– attach the cluster between 60 and 90 seconds after first touching the teat; – suspend the cluster directly beneath the cow (long tube lengthways, weight of cluster distributed evenly between the teats); – make sure that claws and short milk tubes are not twisted.
Points to watch:		
– residue from pre-treatment agents must not get into the milk; *– some dairy industries do not allow the use of disinfectants for pre-dipping, or only under strict conditions;*	*– 60 to 90 second waiting time: hang a clock with a seconds-hand on the wall;* *– avoid transferring/splashing mastitic milk to other teats;*	*– don't allow air sucking;* *– keep the cluster clean;* *– when the cluster stimulates the udder, attach it immediately. Set to milkflow-controlled stimulation.*

Why we do this:

3. Milking	4. Detaching the cluster	5. Dipping/spraying
The right cluster position and the right tension on the teat cup ensures that the cow milks out evenly.	When the milk flow falls below 0.5 l/min, this is the best time to detach the cluster in terms of teat health and milk yield.	The teat opening stays open for a while after milking. Dipping/spraying kills bacteria around the opening, preventing udder infections.

3. Milking

- check the position of the cluster and teat cups (use tube guides);
- check that the cows are not agitated.

4. Detaching the cluster

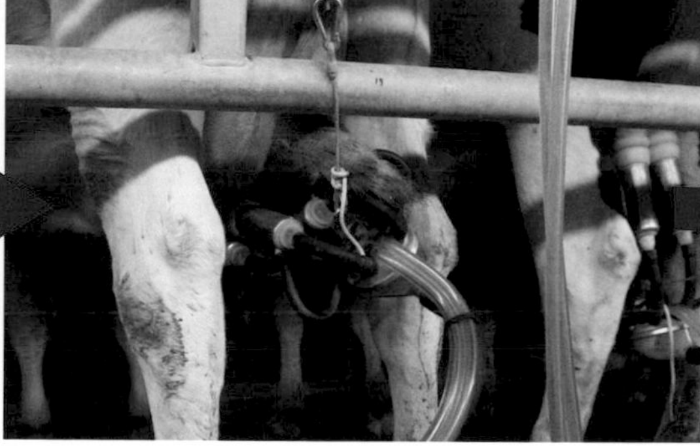

- first switch off the cluster vacuum;
- remove the cluster from the teats very gently; preferably by letting air in at the same time;
- examine the teats and udder.

5. Dipping/spraying

- make sure that at least the lower two-thirds of the teat are completely coated. This is much easier with dipping.

Points to watch:

3. Milking	4. Detaching the cluster	5. Dipping/spraying
– agitation among the cows is a sign of distress and the probability of poor milking out; *– check the milking machine if more than 1 in 10 clusters falls off.*	*– kicking during cluster removal may be a sign of discomfort or pain (no more than 1 in 10 cows should do this);* *– checking the settings for automatic removal is a job for a specialist.*	*– use a disinfecting dip/spray.*

Looking and seeing

There is a knack to identifying and checking as many points as possible in your daily routine. You should know why you are checking and what to do if something is OK or not. Try always to be open to Unclassified Notable Observations (UNOs).

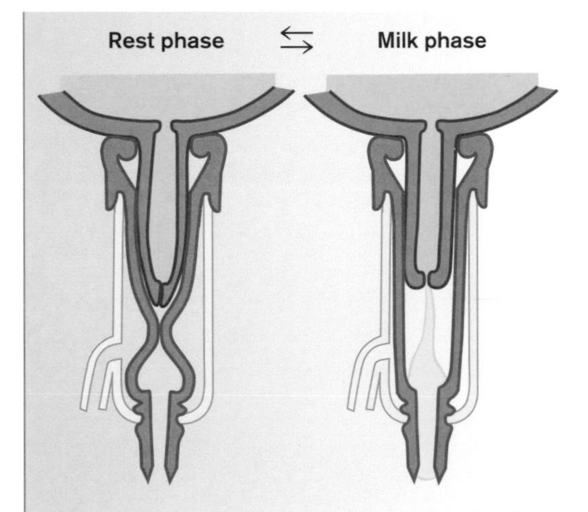

Milking puts a heavy strain on the teat, causing the teat wall and end to swell slightly. Recovery takes around eight hours. If all teats are soft, dry, pink and pain-free when they come out of the teat cup, you know the machine is milking properly.

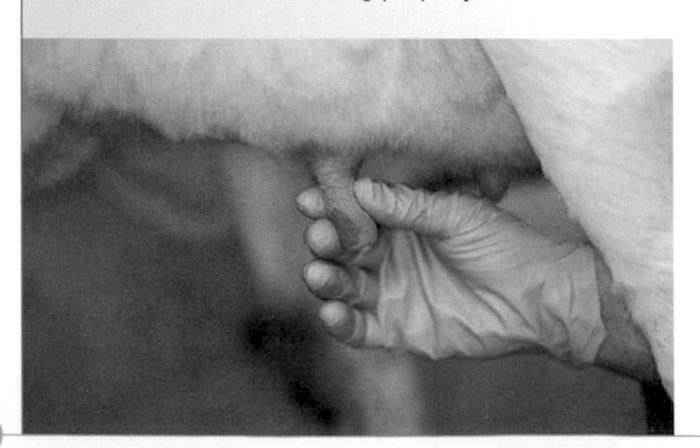

A poor parlour layout causes problems for cows leaving the milking parlour. This can hold up milking and you may be tempted to move cows along, which causes agitation to them and other cows. Consider obstacles such as slippery floors, steps up and down, and other cows. The problem here is a tight, narrow bend.

To do before the next milking:

- *enter all cow information in the records;*
- *clean all the clusters and replace perished tubes;*
- *clean the operator's pit and equipment;*
- *replace all used materials;*
- *optimise lighting and working comfort;*
- *start or plan all improvements (such as replacing bulbs).*

Air sucking poses a risk for mastitis. It suddenly reduces the vacuum under the other teats. There is a risk that milk will flow from one teat cup to another, together with any bacteria present. Not only that, but fluctuations in vacuum may cause drops of milk to be sucked into the teat.

After attaching the cluster there should be no pauses in the milk flow. The free milk from the cistern comes first, then the let-down milk should follow without interruption.

Teat score

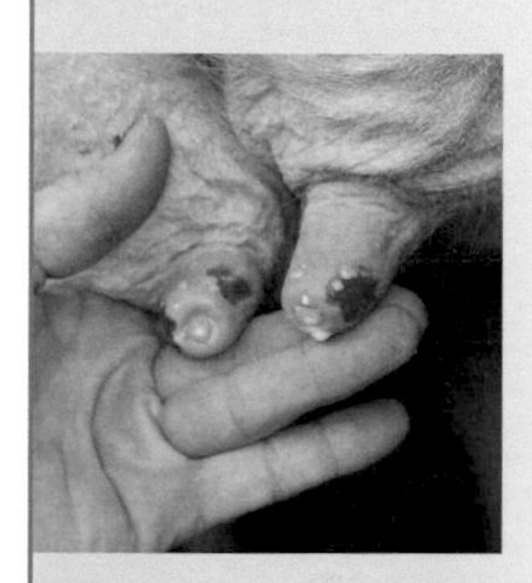

Wet teat

If the teats are clearly wet after detaching the cluster, the milk claw is taking the milk away too slowly. As a result, milk in the teat cup can flow back into the teat. This can result in the udder becoming infected with bacteria from its own skin, or bacteria from the milk or skin of a previous cow.

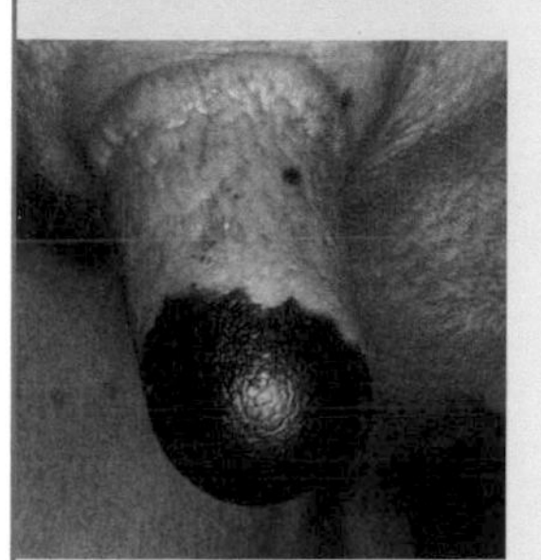

Mouthpiece ring

As long as the liner surrounds the teat properly, the vacuum in the mouthpiece is much lower than under the teat end. If the teats are small (i.e. with heifers) or the liners too large, the vacuum in the mouthpiece chamber becomes too great and the cluster rides up. This often leads to a painful build-up of blood in the teat end, which makes the cow agitated. This can also occur with wet pre-treatment.

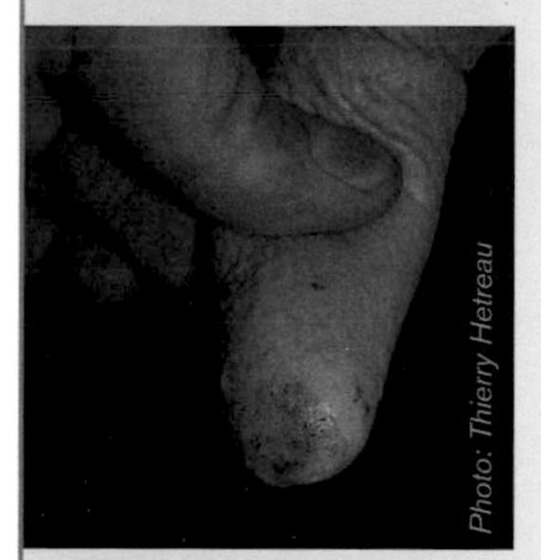

Photo: Thierry Hetreau

Tiny blood spots

Excessive vacuum at the teat end causes tiny blood spots in the skin of the teat. These are accompanied by a painful build-up of blood in the teat end, which will make the cow agitated.

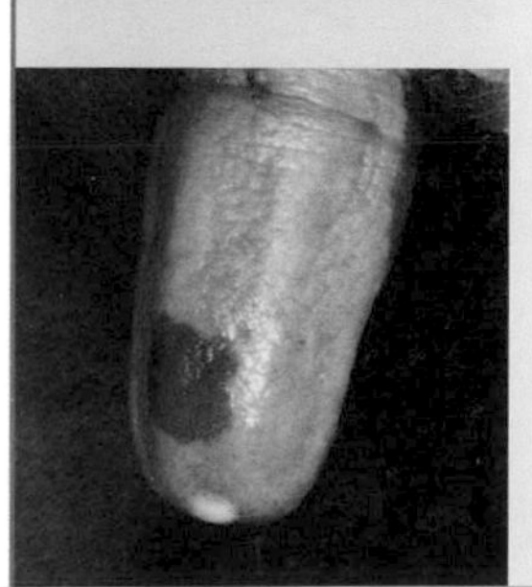

Flat teat

The pinched area develops because the teat was compressed in the liner. The cause is either a worn or stiff/loose liner, or too long a rest phase of the pulsator.

Teat end hyperkeratosis (hardening)

Score the teat ends every three months. This should be done just after removing the milking cluster. Too much hardening indicates that the teat end is being exposed to excessive forces. Carry out a dynamic milking assessment if more than 1 cow in 10 has a pronounced teat ring (score 3 or 4).

Causes of hyperkeratosis:
- milking vacuum too high;
- milking of the cow takes too long;
- overmilking when the quarter is empty;
- incorrect milk/rest phase (pulsator setting);
- the liner not fitting the teats.

Score 1:	Score 2:	Score 3:	Score 4:
no ring	smooth or slightly rough ring	moderately rough rings with a few fronds of keratin	very rough rings with many fronds of keratin

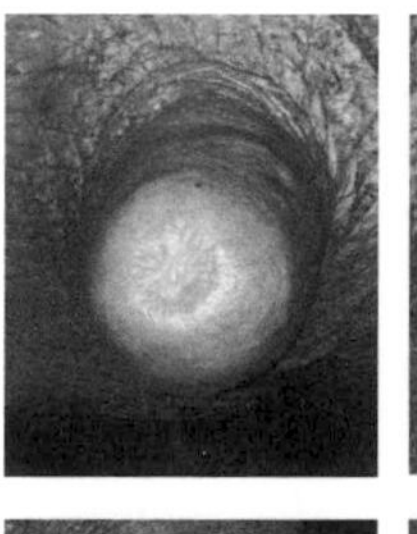
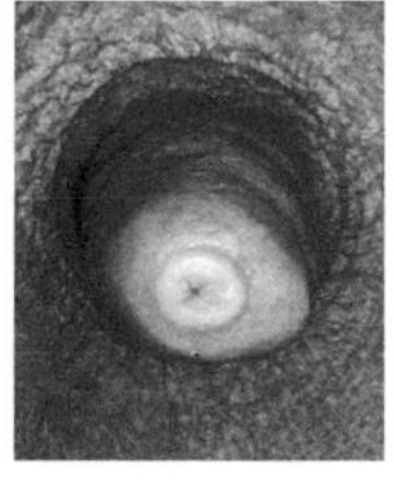
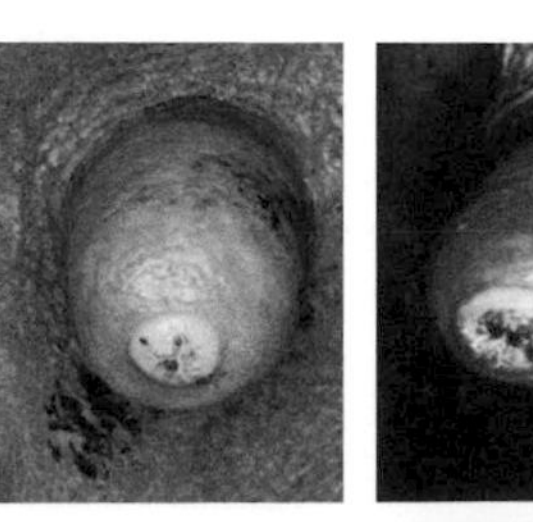
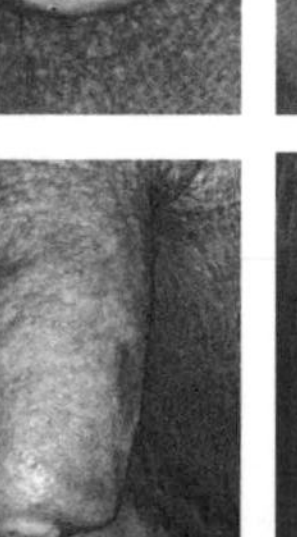
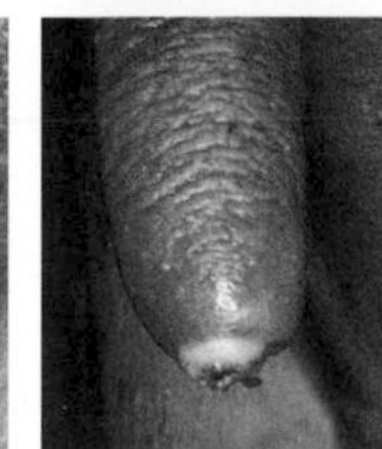

(Photography: ASG Veehouderij, Wageningen University and Research Centre)

The milking robot

Made-to-measure technology

The milking robot can milk high-yielding cows frequently (up to 4x/day) and low-yielding cows less frequently (1.5-2x/day). The norm is one milking to every ten litres of daily production. If the interval between milkings is less than six hours the teats do not recover sufficiently. Over-long milking intervals lower udder resistance. This is because immune cells in freshly produced milk are more active, since they function on energy reserves derived from the blood.

Differences from parlour to parlour

Milking robots work in exactly the same way every time. They can be tailored to the cow and the quarter, e.g. by detaching the teat cup quarter by quarter to minimise stress on the teats. The robot also provides a stream of information about itself, the cows and the milk. This enables the dairy farmer to identify abnormalities and problems, such as frequency of visits, refusals and number of failed milkings, at a very early stage. New techniques measure the quality of the milk from each quarter (including electrical conductivity, colour, temperature and cell count) with ever-increasing accuracy.

Magnification effect

One milking robot can milk sixty cows three times a day. If something goes wrong it can have direct consequences for all cows and all milkings. An example is pre-treatment or spraying errors.

Success depends on methodical checking and immediate action

Check at least twice a day: Robot: frequency of visits and alerts. Shed: feed intake, water, health.
Even slightly lame and weak cows don't visit the robot often enough. Such cows both develop and cause problems. If they don't eat enough their resistance falls.

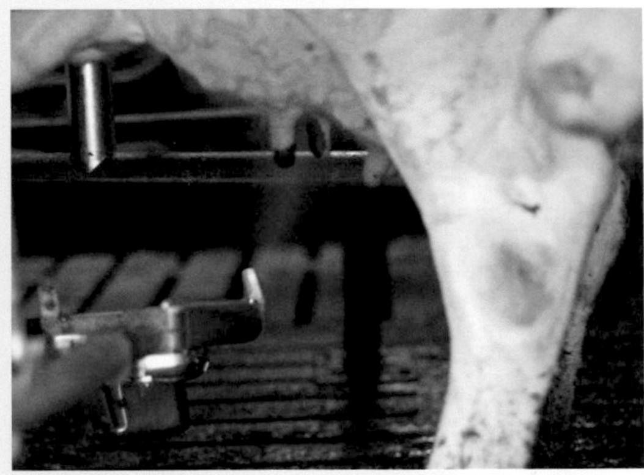

Check three times a day that the robot is pre-treating, milking and spraying properly. Teat disinfection is a basic cornerstone of udder health. Can you tell right away when the spray has run out? Milking robots can't dip, not yet anyway. Therefor, viscous dips such as barrier dips can not be used.

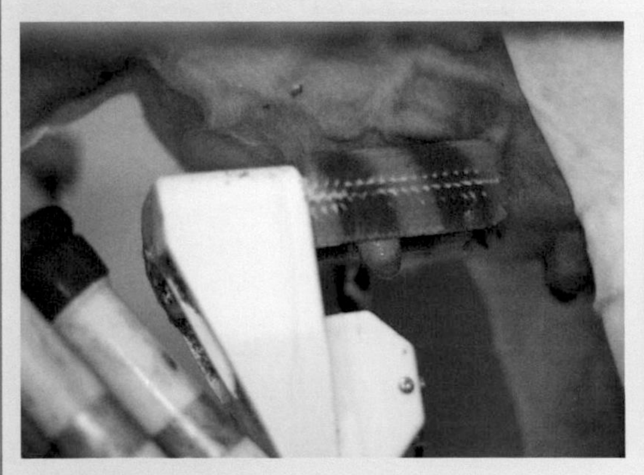

Dirty udders pose even more problems for a robot than they do for a milker, so cows and udders should be very clean at all times. This means first-rate nutrition, comfortable and clean cubicles, clean floors, and keeping udders and tails closely shorn.

Conductivity alerts are the most important daily check for mastitis. A new alert means that the cow and its udder should be checked immediately (palpation, removal, CMT). If the milk is abnormal, treat the animal immediately in accordance with the farm treatment plan.

The milking parlour

The fundamentals of milking in a group pen are the same as in a milking parlour or using a robot. However, it does take more discipline to keep the interval between pre-treatment and cluster attachment between 60 and 90 seconds for each cow. Too long or too short an interval results in a longer milking time, and probably less milk and more udder problems. Technical aids such as a rail for the milking clusters make the work lighter and easier, enabling you to work more smoothly and efficiently. Due to the long, high milk pipes, the installation and operation of the milking machine in a group pen can be very different. Keep to a regular maintenance schedule and if you have any doubts get an expert in to check your milking machine and milking technique by means of a dynamic milking assessment. In some countries cows are still tied.

Where does this milk end up? Keep lying places clean, dry and free from milk residue.

Milk high cell count cows with a separate milking cluster. Mark them and/or keep them together at the end of the row.

Even in a group pen, you still need skill and dedication to keep cows strong and healthy. Do all animals have enough feed/water/light/air/rest and space? Is tasty feed always available? Is each cow's neighbour eating as well? Does the drinking trough provide enough water and can the cow reach it? Without a comfortable place to lie down, cows in a group pen will overload their hooves and develop thick hocks and knees. Their resistance and production will fall. Lying area for a Friesian Holstein cow measuring 1.47 m at the withers: length 1.80 m, width 1.35 m. With a soft floor providing good grip. Rear edge of feed trough: max. 20 cm and rounded. Withers bar: 1.22 m high, 40 cm in front of rear edge of feed trough. Inadequate light results in poor oestrus and poor working conditions. Make sure the light level is 200 lux, 16 hours a day. Finally, cows need constant fresh air at their nostrils. If the shed temperature is over 21°C or so, a light breeze through the shed is desir.

Working methodically

This cow is now giving twelve litres of milk a day and is ready to be dried off. The farmer uses dry cow therapy in line with the farm treatment plan and trims her feet to ensure that she calves with healthy, well-formed hooves.

Today

If you do your day-to-day work well, you can expect a positive outcome. But how do you know if you're working well? Very few people are objective enough to judge and improve their own performance. Most of us need a bit of help.

Tomorrow

Managing udder health means thinking ahead. Cows and their conditions change constantly, so keep looking to the future and take advice. How do you prevent problems due to heat stress? How do you cope with too much or too little grass growth? What will happen in the cowshed if you take on another five cows? Be aware that you have a completely new herd in your shed every four years. Will the liners still fit their teats?

Besides your daily routine, you also have jobs to do on certain days of the week or month. Some of this work, such as drying off and introducing replacement heifers, is done on specific days. Some of it is unplanned, such as calving. Following a weekly and monthly schedule will help you organise your work efficiently and make sure you do the right things at the right time.

Are you working well? What are your current results like?

Fixed schedule

Preventive jobs in particular are easily forgotten, because they're not urgent and the results aren't immediately obvious. But this is precisely the sort of work that can be planned, minimising the number of problems that arise. Problems are always urgent and take up more time than you can afford.
Make sure the results of preventive work are obvious, by using monthly cow health summaries, for example. Set yourself achievable targets. This has a motivating effect and helps you manage the farm properly.

Last month's results:

	Target:	*Our result:*
- tank cell count:	*125,000*	*122,000*
- udder inflammation	*less than 3*	*2*
- new alerts	*less than 10%*	*11%*
- dead calves	*0*	*0*
- newly calved cows with fever	*max. 2 in 10*	*2 in 11*
- % inseminated at 100 days	*75%*	*69%*
- % non-inseminated at 150 days	*less than 10%*	*7%*
- pregnancy rate	*55%*	*48%*

Getting a checkup

A proven success factor is a monthly review of the udder health of the herd and individual cows, followed up by targeted action. How do you organise this?

Procedure for a discussion with an advisor:

1. Preparation:
- agree points for discussion;
- prepare points for discussion.
2. Introduction:
- the aim or aims of the discussion;
- decide who will lead the discussion;
- time available.
3. Discussion:
- facts and options (establishing the situation);
- pros and cons, risks and opportunities (forming an opinion);
- what are you going to do (reaching a decision).
4. Conclusion:
- summarise decisions and agreements;
- make follow-up arrangements.

Plan a scheduled discussion with an advisor after the monthly milk inspection result. Choose advisers who are not afraid to be blunt or critical. Give them access to your management data via the Internet so they can prepare fully for each contact.

Draw up a list of points for discussion:

1. ***Farm results (key statistics):***
   - tank cell count;
   - percentage of cows with a high cell count;
   - percentage of new alerts;
   - number of cows with udder inflammation;
   - number of problems associated with calving;
   - energy supply at start of lactation;
   - number of treatments and use of veterinary medicines.
   Action:
   - determine and introduce improvements if necessary.

2. ***All cows with a high cell count:***
   - *How/when are you going to treat them? At drying-off? Are you going to cull?*
   - *Have you treated? What were the results? What next?*
   - *Which cows do you mark as high-risk animals (sources of infection)?*

   Action:
   - *treat, dry off, cull;*
   - *mark high cell count cows and/or put them in a separate group.*
   - *In the case of recovered cows, remove mark and/or return them to the herd.*

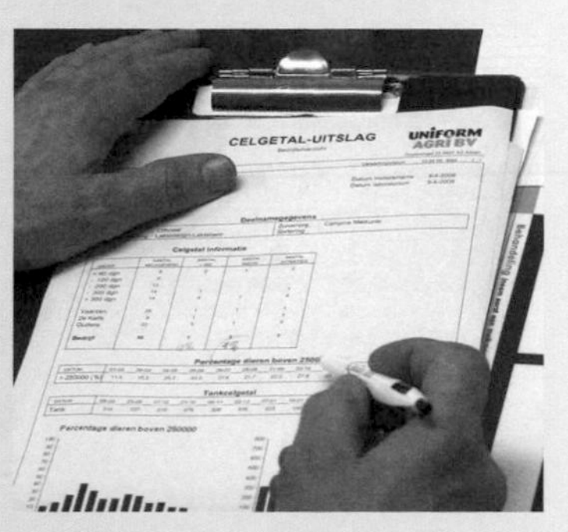

3. ***Points for action from previous month:***
   - *Has everything been done that should have been done?*
   - *Were the desired results achieved? If not: what do you do now?*

4. ***Look forward to next month:***
   - *Are any changes in management expected (different procedures, new farm worker, different shed layout/arrangement of groups)?*
   - *Are any major stresses expected (heat, flies, turnout/housing, changes in diet/new silage)?*
   - *Are you expecting any other important events (milk machine inspection, going on a training course)?*

Check and co-ordinate

Good farmers constantly check whether they and their milking machine are doing their work properly. But it is easy to stop noticing where improvements can be made and so using a system and advisors to check farm management can help maintain high standards and to keep up to date with new developments and so ensure that the farm progresses. Use a checking and improvement system for your milking. It should include the annual equipment overhaul, a six-monthly comprehensive dynamic milking assessment and three-monthly teat scoring.

Be prepared for cow losses due to disease and accidents. Put the milking procedure down on paper, so that a relief worker can take over the reins smoothly.

The value of good milking

If you are milking your cows well, you have 50% of your udder health under control. A good milker has 25% less mastitis and a 15% shorter milking time than an average milker. Make sure all milkers are working in the same way and to the same standard. It is impossible to make up for a bad milker. All farms should have at least two people milking.

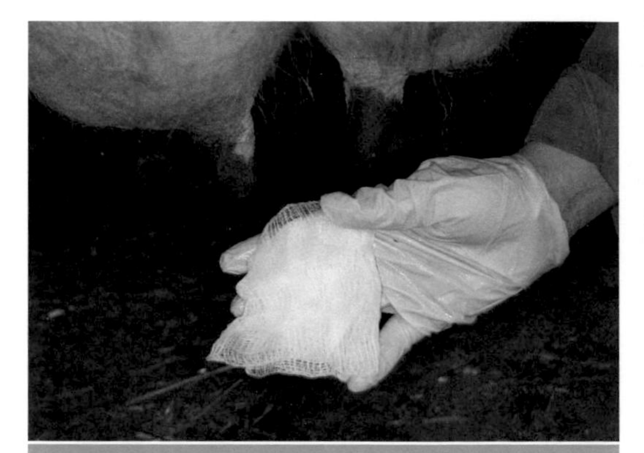

If you wipe the teat end with a dry cloth after preparation you can tell how well the teat end has been cleaned. This teat end was nice and clean.

Good preparation and well-timed cluster attachment

The cow's milk let-down reflex is stimulated by the hormone oxytocin, which is carried from the brain to the udder in the bloodstream. The brain releases oxytocin in response to stimulation of the teats and the teat end in particular. Foremilk stripping is the most powerful stimulus. Other strong stimuli are massaging the teat end, teat and udder. There is about one minute response time between stimulation and sufficient milk flow. If you attach the cluster 60 to 90 seconds after thorough preparation, you will get a good, strong milk flow. If the preparation is poor and/or the cluster is attached too soon, there will be a period with no milk let down shortly after attachment. The low oxytocin level results in a short milk peak and an ever-decreasing milk flow, so that the cow milks out slowly. If you attach too late, the oxytocin level remains too low and the milk flow is also slower. Cows become accustomed to being stripped by hand and to oxytocin injections. If cows are prepared well you will need oxytocin only in cases of mastitis and sometimes with newly calved heifers. Hand-stripping should be unnecessary. Agitation and stress inhibit the release of oxytocin, hence the importance of calm before and during milking.

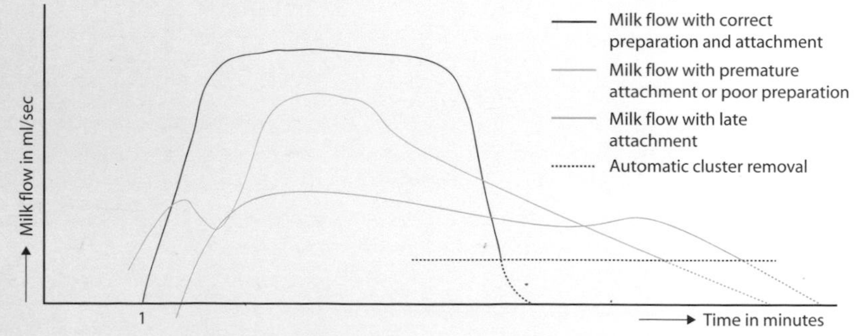

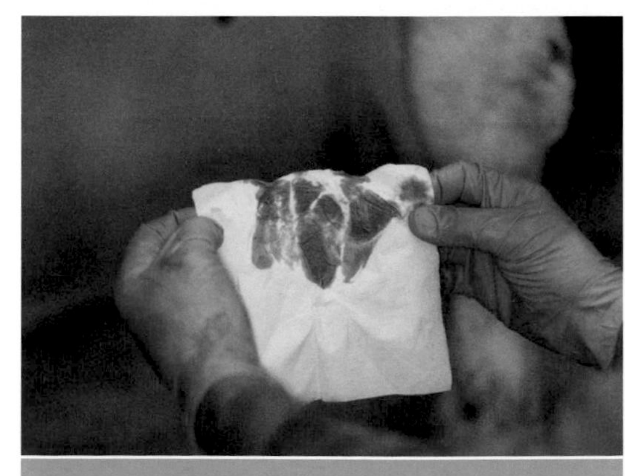

You can check how well you are spraying or dipping by wrapping a paper towel round a teat. This teat has been dipped properly.

Do not forget to check the separate cluster for the newly calved cows.

Be open to criticism and improvement

Top cattle farmers are genuinely open to criticism, new techniques and new procedures. On the one hand they are constantly asking themselves questions; on the other, they are able to make decisions and stick to a course of action once embarked upon.

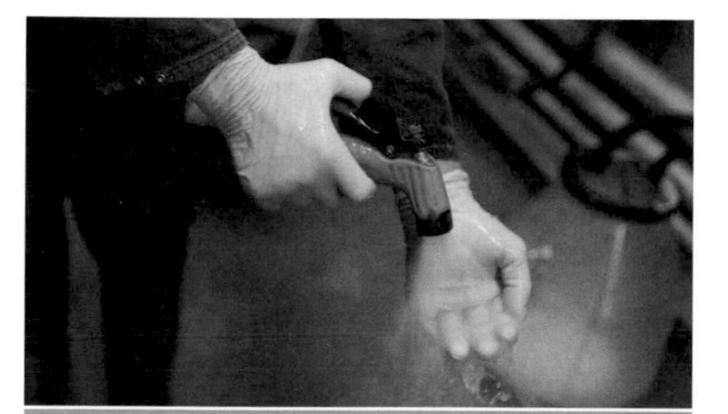

Gloves help you work more cleanly because they retain less dirt and are easier to spray clean. But they take some getting used to.

Udder hair singeing should be done every six weeks, clipping two or three times a year. Choose whichever suits you, as long as the udders stay clean.

Dynamic milking assessment

In a 'wet' or dynamic milking assessment, the milking machine, milker and cows are monitored during milking. This tells you if machine and milker are working properly. It also allows the expert to assess other factors affecting udder health, such as cow shed hygiene, nutrition and the general health of the cows.

During a service, the technician makes sure the milking machine is technically up to spec, but a dynamic assessment reveals whether the system as a whole is actually working properly. Here, the pressure in the short and long milk tube is being measured.

With an ergonomic layout and the right preparation, attachment, milking, detachment and dipping procedures, the cow will repay you with good health and high yield, and working time is also reduced.

The transparent teat cup shows that the milk is not flowing away quickly enough, 'washing' the teat end. This results in a higher risk of infection. Wet teats after cluster removal are a sign of teat washing. Note: due to overmilking, teats that have in fact been washed may be dry when they come out of the teat cups.

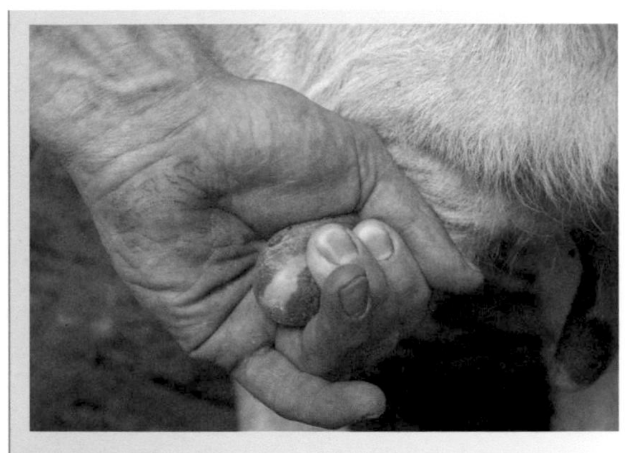

An intact, closed teat opening gives the best protection against infection, although keratin fronds are a risk. In half of dry cows the teat opening is sealed after a week. This may differ from farm to farm, however. For example, advanced teat end hyperkeratosis at drying-off hampers the sealing of the teat opening. In one or two cows in every ten, the teat opening fails to seal completely during the dry period.

What do you do about this cow?

This cow is supposed to have been dried off. What do you do?

Repeat the dry cow therapy after three days if the cow is still leaking a lot of milk. Keep lying areas clean and control flies. There is no point in using more than one intramammary tube per quarter, or another tube further up in the dry period.

Conscientious management

The dry period serves as a recovery phase for the cow and her udder. The optimum length is six weeks for second calvers and older cows, eight weeks for first-time calvers. However, these guidelines apply subject to strict pre-conditions. First, the cow should be giving less than fifteen litres a day at drying-off. Second, you should work systematically so that, very exceptionally, a cow is dried off two weeks either side of the guideline. Reduce the milk yield by giving a cow the diet for cows early in their dry period for a few days before drying off. Bear in mind that the reduced feed intake may make her susceptible to milk fever and ketosis.

Dry period and udder health

The dry period is an extremely important time for udder health for three reasons. First, some of the cases of mastitis in the first month after calving are the result of infections during the dry period. Second, the first few weeks after calving are a time of greatly lowered resistance for the cow: during this period a third of clinical cases of mastitis occur. The degree to which her resistance is lowered depends heavily on the cow's nutrition and care during the dry period and around calving. Third, the dry period is a good time for the long-term treatment of cows with a high cell count.

Dry cow tubes

A vet can help you draw up a farm treatment plan that tells the best dry cow therapy per cow, covering antibiotics and teat sealants. The most appropriate antibiotics differ from farm to farm. Antibiotics are used to cure existing infections (high cell count) and to prevent new ones. Certain antibiotics are effective against Gram-positive bacteria such as Streptococci and Staphylococci, but less so against Gram-negative bacteria such as *E. coli*.

New and healthy udder tissue

The renewal of udder tissue does not begin until all the milk has been reabsorbed from the udder. This reabsorption of milk costs the udder tissue a lot of energy and effort. It takes around a week to occur if the cow is producing less than fifteen litres. If the yield is higher it takes much longer and the teat opening does not seal so well, leading to more udder infections. In addition, the white blood cells are busy mopping up milk instead of bacteria. At the start of the dry period the teat opening is not yet fully sealed, the cow is still producing milk and the animal's general resistance is reduced due to stress. At the end of the dry period the antibiotics are wearing off, the milk is returning, the teat opening may open and resistance falls due to lack of energy, calcium deficiency, hormones and stress.

The dry period

Nutrition and care around calving

Dry cows should take in exactly the right amount of energy, protein, vitamins and minerals to enable them to start their next lactation fit and healthy. Make sure every cow is eating the correct diet. A dry period diet is made-to-measure, based on the characteristics of the feeds used and the method of feeding. The basic principles for a good transition diet are:

- a negative cation/anion balance to combat milk fever, oedema and excessive colostrum production;
- good rumination due to adequate fibre;
- crude protein content of around 12% for cows and 14 to 15% for heifers;
- simultaneous intake of easily digestible feed components with roughage, in a safe proportion, to avoid rumen acidosis;
- every cow should have permanent access to sufficient tasty feed.

Check daily that every dry cow:

Is eating enough and is eating the correct diet:
– rumen fill;
– feeding behaviour (selecting/not selecting);
– dung digestion and consistency (no difference between cows);
– condition score (weekly).
Is drinking enough:
– availability of clean drinking water;
– dryness of dung.
Is lying and moving about enough:
– intact hocks;
– enough space in the cubicle;
– plenty of space to walk about.
Is healthy:
– udder;
– hooves.
Is exposed to low infection pressure:
– hygiene score;
– flies;
– adequate provision of clean, dry lying areas.
Has an appropriate climate and ventilation.

Milk inspection reports reveal whether the nutrition of individual cows and groups of cows is up to standard. Production, fat and protein content and the ratio between the latter provide invaluable information in this respect.

Dung always contains E. coli, and soiled bedding can contain all or any of the mastitis bacteria. Cows in milk and newly calved cows run a greatly reduced risk of udder infections in dry, clean pens. Never put a cow in milk in a pen that has held a sick cow without first cleaning and disinfecting the pen.

The cubicles and udders of dry cows should receive the same care and attention as those of milk-producing cows. Pay extra attention to clean cubicles, teat dips and cow checks during the first and last two weeks of the dry period.

Rearing young stock

Good rearing produces top-quality cows

First-class rearing and a smooth introduction into the herd brings strong, productive cows into the house. Hereditary characteristics set the boundaries but rearing determines the potential quality of the heifers. The factors that ensure a perfectly healthy udder are clean, dry accommodation, first-class nutrition and minimal stress around calving. Plus controlling risks such as flies and suckling by other heifers. Activities such as removing accessory teats and vaccinations are an integral part of good rearing.

Are you doing better?

On average, one in eight heifers contracts mastitis during their first lactation, 40% of those in the first month after calving. At the first milk inspection, one in five heifers have subclinical mastitis. This means that they have a cell count over 150,000. At calving, around half of heifers have an udder infection. A third of those cases involves coagulase negative Staphylococci, which don't usually cause problems. The rest are mastitis bacteria such as *S. aureus, E. coli* and Streptococci.

Don't feed mastitic milk

Young calves suck and suckle each other. If the suckling calf has recently drunk mastitic milk and then suckles another heifer's udder, the suckled udder is at risk of becoming infected with mastitis bacteria. Mastitic milk can also infect calves with paratuberculosis (Johne's disease), mycoplasma and resistant bacteria.

Controlling flies helps to prevent udder problems in young animals. Flies transmit mastitis bacteria such as S. aureus and can cause summer mastitis. Summer mastitis is an incurable udder infection that occurs mainly in pregnant heifers and dry cows at pasture.

A calf learns to suckle an udder during its milk-drinking phase. Identify sucklers as soon as possible and remove them from the herd or insert a special nose ring. Suckling bruises the teats, which may cause deformities resulting in blind or blocked teats. Suckling stimulates pregnant heifers to produce milk, bringing a risk of mastitis.

Heifer mastitis is usually caused by soiled cubicles, flies, suckling, soiled calving pens and during milking - after calving. Lowered resistance of the heifer is an important contributing factor. The main causes of lowered resistance are stress, mineral deficiency (especially selenium, copper and magnesium), udder oedema and difficult calving.

Introducing heifers

Introduction of heifers

The introduction of heifers into the dairy herd starts eight to six weeks before calving. The animals are undergoing major changes during this period, such as a new diet, new accommodation, new herdmates, udder development, calving and producing milk. The health and production of heifers at the end of this period depends on how they start it. Are they healthy? Are they well-developed? Are they familiar with the cubicles, feed barrier and feed? Is their mineral status in order? During their introduction heifers should become familiar with the dairy herd and the cowshed.

Groups

Heifers are best introduced to the dry cows where there is the most supervision, the most suitable diet and – if all is well – the lowest infection pressure. If the basic diet permits, the heifers may also spend two weeks in the herd first and then four to six weeks with the dry cows. Provided the farmer works calmly and takes his time, the heifer need not join the herd until after calving. A separate production group comprised of heifers gives the fewest problems and the highest production. Crowded cowsheds and difficult access to feed give the most trouble.

Success factors:
No stress.
Optimum nutrition.
Clean environment.
Strong and healthy.

If a heifer is leaking a lot of colostrum before calving, milk her. Give her calf previously (frozen) colostrum from another cow.

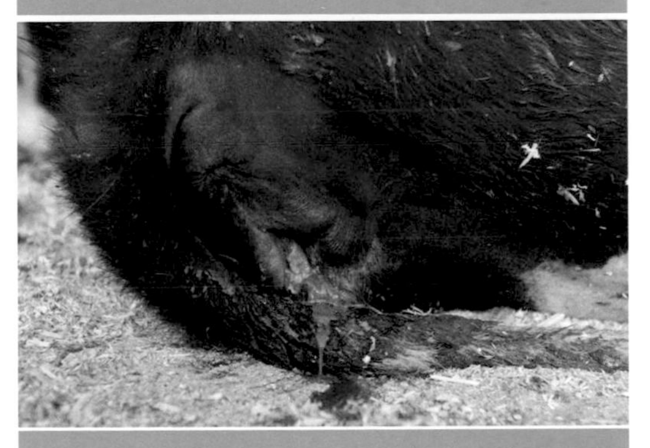

This painful birth canal is reducing the cow's feed intake and increasing her risk of uterine and other infections. Use bulls that produce small calves. During calving, keep the heifer calm and allow her time to stretch the birth canal properly. If you assist with calving, do so hygienically and competently. Practise with your vet and know how to treat a bruised birth canal.

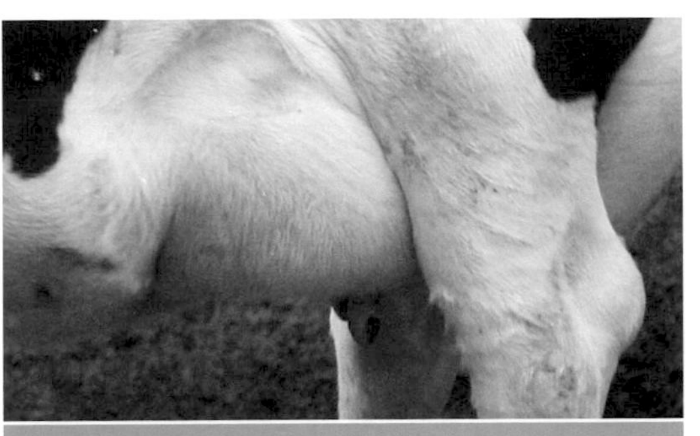

Udder oedema stops the udder milking out properly and increases the risk of mastitis and teat problems. Although the cause is unknown, we do know that udder oedema is minimised with diets that have a low cation/anion balance, which increase milk production slightly (such as a good dry cow diet).

Make sure young animals have sufficient numbers of comfortable cubicles. This should stop them lying in passageways and will reduce udder contamination from slurry and decrease the risk of infection. Milk-producing cows that lie in the passageways contract mastitis easily and are often culled as a result.

The CMT

The CMT involves mixing a small sample of milk with an equal volume of test liquid. If the milk has a cell count over 400,000, the resulting liquid is viscous. The test liquid consists of 3% sodium lauryl sulphate, sometimes with additives such as a colouring agent. The test tray or segmented test paddle is available from specialist suppliers.

Carry out a CMT to find out if a quarter has a cell count over 400,000

Carrying out a CMT

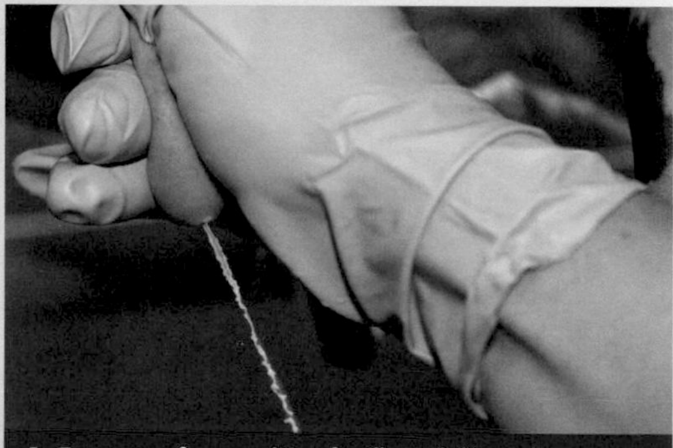

1. Express a few squirts of milk and discard. Express two squirts of milk from each quarter into separate compartments.

2. Always hold the paddle under the cow in the same way, e.g. with the handle towards its head.

3. Pour excess milk out of the compartments (not onto the parlour floor) until the level reaches the guidelines.

4. Add an equal volume of test liquid and rotate for a minute to mix the contents.

Reading the result

Both photos show thickening in the bottom left compartment: that milk has a cell count over 400,000. The milk in the other three compartments shows no reaction.

Taking milk samples

Bacteriological testing

If you take a milk sample from each evident case of mastitis you can have the bacteria responsible cultured. Take the sample before administering any drugs and store in the freezer. Every farm should have a procedure for taking and sending in milk samples. For example, you can take samples from cows with a high cell count every month and send them in with the frozen samples. A sample will remain usable in the freezer for at least a year. This enables you to have a group of samples cultured if there is a change in mastitis levels. Having a good idea of the causes of mastitis on the farm will enable you to draw up an effective prevention and treatment plan.

Treating a cow

You have been treating a cow with antibiotics for three days in accordance with the treatment plan, but the mastitis doesn't seem to be getting any better. What do you do?

1. Consult your vet about further treatment; continuing with the same treatment usually gives a better result than changing the treatment.
2. Bacteriological testing may show that the cow has a form of mastitis that is difficult to treat and calls for different measures (i.e. yeast, prototheca, klebsiella, mycoplasma), or that the bacteria are resistant to the antibiotic used.

Taking a milk sample

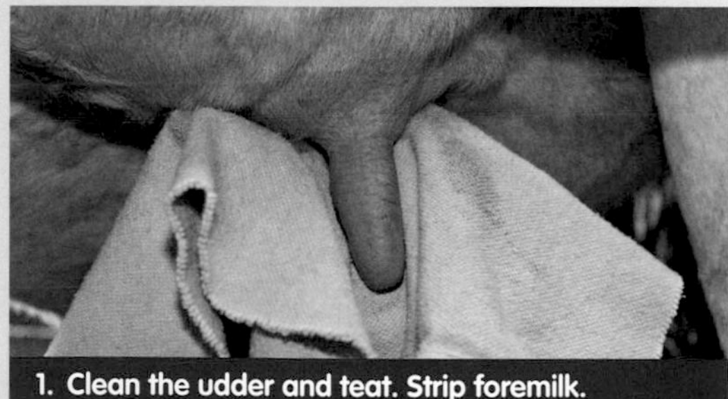

1. Clean the udder and teat. Strip foremilk.

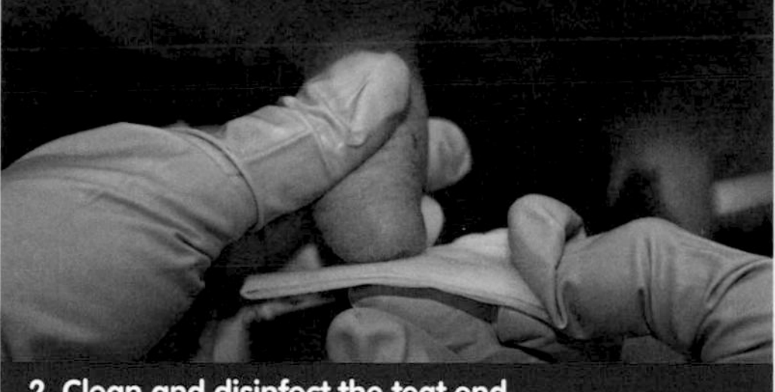

2. Clean and disinfect the teat end.

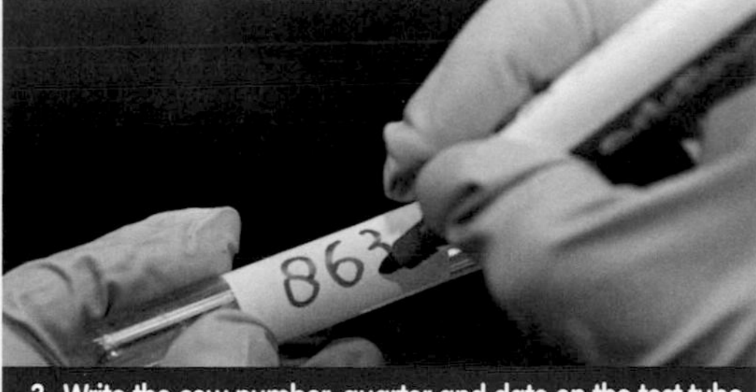

3. Write the cow number, quarter and date on the test tube.

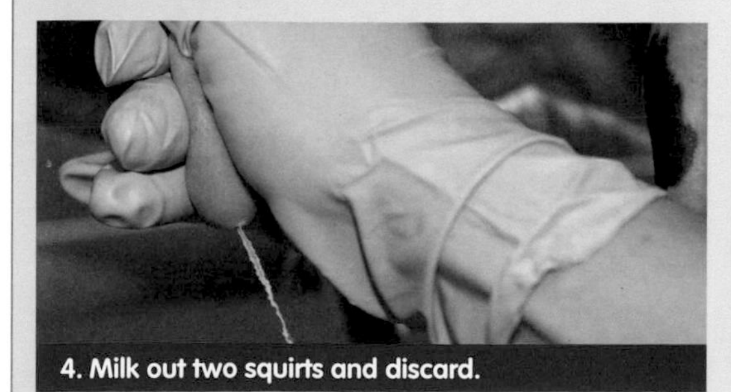

4. Milk out two squirts and discard.

5. Make sure there is no dust in the tube or cover.

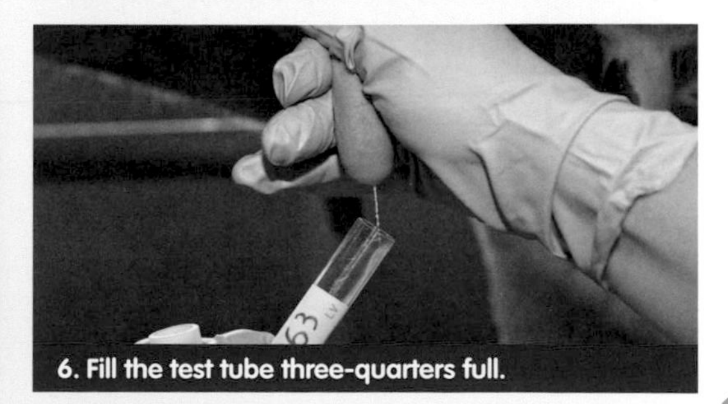

6. Fill the test tube three-quarters full.

The five-point plan:

This five-point plan shows the five areas for attention that determine udder health on a farm. Beside each area, the factors for success are described. If the factors for success are in order, you have the relevant area under control.

Infection pressure:
- *make sure the cow's surroundings are clean and dry;*
- *make sure there are no sources of infection such as infected cows (including bought-in cows), water or bedding.*

Resistance:
- *make sure the food supply and intake meet the needs of every cow at each point in her life and lactation cycle;*
- *the same applies to water;*
- *make sure every cow always has a comfortable place to lie down and can walk about in safety and comfort;*
- *make sure cow and udder health are first-rate;*
- *make sure all cows have optimum temperature and ventilation.*

Monitoring:
- *set targets for udder health on your farm: number of clinical cases of mastitis, tank cell count and % of new cases;*
- *keep accurate and detailed records of mastitis, cell count, treatments, animals cured and culled, and all changes;*
- *check on a monthly basis: % new infections, number of clinical cases of mastitis, bacteriological test results, tank cell count and nutrition;*
- *review your udder health policy and procedures annually and whenever there is an increase in levels of mastitis.*

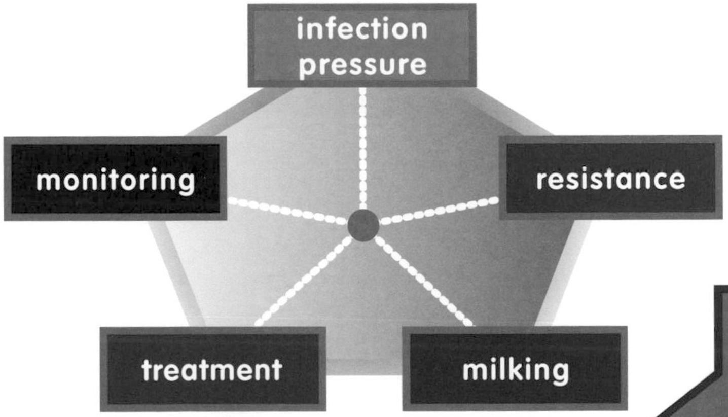

infection pressure
monitoring
resistance
treatment
milking

Milking:
- *identify infected animals as early as possible;*
- *treat immediately, methodically and consistently, have a protocol for culling problem cows;*
- *administer medicines correctly;*
- *make sure the recovering cow is properly cared for and looked after;*
- *give every cow appropriate dry cow therapy;*
- *make sure the farm treatment plan is up to date.*

Treatment:
- *identify infected animals as early as possible;*
- *treat immediately, methodically and consistently, have a protocol for culling problem cows;*
- *administer medicines correctly;*
- *make sure the recovering cow is properly cared for and looked after;*
- *give every cow appropriate dry cow therapy;*
- *make sure the farm treatment plan is up to date.*

Memory aid

A memory aid can help you remember these areas for attention.

For example:
***I** **R**eally **M**ust **T**ackle **M**astitis*

Expertise, management and business acumen

Besides expertise, udder health also calls for good management and business acumen.
In your capacity as farm manager, review the structure and performance of your and your colleagues' work two or three times a year. Is this being done efficiently? Is it yielding the desired results? Is it pleasant work? Does everyone have enough knowledge and the right tools to do their work well? What does "well" mean? From a business point of view, take a regular look at your objectives, resources and results. Draw up a plan for the year as part of a long-term perspective. Where do you want to be in a year's time? And in five years' time? What are your objectives for the coming year? How are you going to achieve them, and what will you need to do this? How well are you performing compared with other farms? Where can you make savings or improvements? Where can you expand? How much can you invest, and where?

Improvements through breeding

Breed for characteristics such as udder health and cell count. A bull with an udder health index of 104 will sire daughters with an average of 3% less mastitis, e.g. 22% instead of 25%.

Breed for ideal external characteristics, such as a milking rate that is not too high or too low and hind leg placement that is not too wide or too narrow.

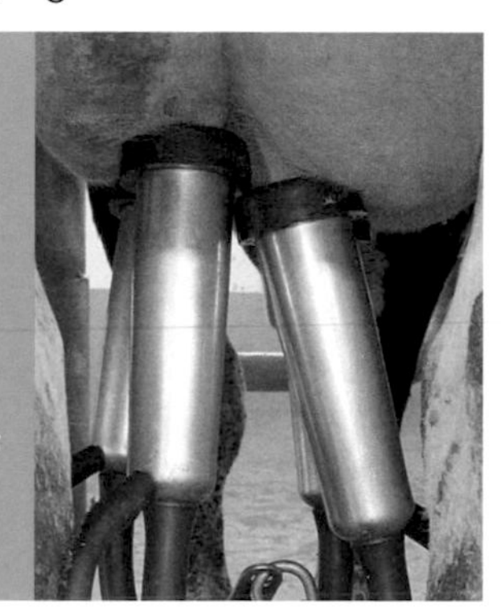

Year plans and budgeting

You are a farm manager and seem to have udder health under control, with a tank cell count of 165,000 and 28 cases of clinical mastitis per 100 cows last year. What do you do?

1. Carry on as normal, not paying particular attention to udder health.
2. Decide to work towards a tank cell count of 140,000 and 20% clinical mastitis.
3. Carry on as you have been doing and draw up a year plan to monitor and improve procedures, cell counts and clinical mastitis.

1. Not a sensible move; if problems arise you will detect them too late and not know how to respond. 2. Sensible and ambitious, calls for a plan of action, plus first-rate management and expertise. 3. Sensible and ambitious, you set targets, work methodically and set aside a given amount (budget) each year for monitoring and improvement.

How much should mastitis control cost?

It is difficult to answer questions such as 'How much can I spend on treatment?' or 'How much do I allocate for the milking machine, the testing of milk samples, etc.?'. Not just because one cow differs from another, but also because certain aspects are hard to express in terms of money. This applies, for example, to utilising the full milk quota, the risk of infection spreading and the additional work and worry caused by clinical mastitis.

Losses due to clinical mastitis:

In the first three months of lactation:	*€ 280*
In months four to nine:	*€ 170*
On average:	*€ 225*

This calculation does not include the risk of antibiotics in the tank, the additional work involved or the extra milking time.

Losses due to a high cell count:

Tank cell count	*Loss of production in kg/day:*
50,000	*0 kg/day*
100,000	*– 0.7 kg/day*
200,000	*– 1.4 kg/day*
400,000	*– 2.1 kg/day*

Besides their lower production, cows with a high cell count are a constant source of infection for other cows. On farms with a high tank cell count the milkers don't register more clinical mastitis. The question rises: whether they are observing well enough?

Best treatment with treatment plan

A farm treatment plan describes the treatment that offers the best chance of recovery. This doesn't mean that all cases of mastitis will recover. And it doesn't mean that in every instance you have to resort to antibiotics. If you always follow a treatment plan precisely, you can be sure you are giving the best possible treatment. Treating an animal means more than simply administering drugs. Only if you always treat in the same way will the vet be able to monitor the outcome and determine whether treatment can be improved, perhaps by changing the drugs used or extending the period of treatment.

Farm treatment plan

A treatment plan should be displayed near the medicine cabinet, say on the door or on the wall beside it. Recording treatments is easy if each treatment has its own code, e.g. mastitis 1 (M1). The farm treatment plan also makes it clear what the stock in the medicine cabinet should look like, i.e. which drugs should be present and in what quantities.

Homoeopathy

Science has not yet been able to demonstrate that homoeopathic medicines have any effect on mastitis.

Chance of recovery and future value

Treat a young, promising cow more intensively. Young animals have a good chance of recovery and will repay the treatment costs with interest. Cases with a low chance of recovery should not be treated but culled. These include cows which have already had a high cell count, cows with infections in more than one quarter, and older cows.

Managing and using the drugs stock is something you get used to. Arrange the drugs in rows, with the oldest at the front. Don't start a new pack until the old one is finished. Every month, clean the cabinet, top up supplies and discard anything that is worn out or out of date.

Testing a milk sample for drug residues indicates conclusively whether the milk can be collected. Especially useful with sick cows, long-term treatment and treatment involving several different drugs. Incorporate a procedure during milking to make sure that mastitic milk never ends up in the milk tank by accident.

Factors for successful treatment:
Early. Structured. Conscientious. Careful.

Keep the cow in mind

Treating an udder infection involves more than just administering antibiotics, because in the end the cow has to cure herself.

Treatment and care

Standard treatment for mastitis:

- Milk the quarter out every four hours, aid with an oxytocin injection.
- If there is swelling or pain, administer an anti-inflammatory (NSAID).
- Make sure the cow drinks plenty of water. Give additional fresh, tepid water if necessary.
- Make sure the cow takes in as much feed as possible with sufficient fibre.
- Make sure the cow can lie down comfortably in fresh and dry surroundings.
- Prevent the transmission of bacteria to other cows.

Special measures

Sick cows need supportive treatment and care. Draw up a standard procedure for this with your vet. Signs of a sick cow are a temperature over 39.5 °C, sluggish and lethargic behaviour, cold ears or cold skin. Sick cows with mastitis belong in a separate hospital pen and certainly not in pens for newly calved cows and cows in calf. Milk newly calved cows first then mastitic ones using a separate milking cluster, not the other way round.

Consider your choice of dip carefully

A contact dip works very quickly but is short-lasting. This is the preferred dip on farms where contagious bacteria are the cause of problems. A barrier dip has a lasting effect, but is slow to work. This is the preferred dip on farms where the pressure of infection from contagious bacteria is low and environmental bacteria are the cause of problems. These dips are usually too viscous for spraying. Only use dips with good disinfecting (bacteria-killing) properties. In addition to disinfectant agents, most dips also contain emollients such as lanolin, glycerin or allantoin which can make chapped, dry teat skin softer and more supple. Teat dipping protects the teat opening against bacterial invasion. Contagious bacteria reach the teat opening with the milk, or grow towards it on the skin of the teat. Teat disinfection kills these bacteria on the teat end. Environmental bacteria come into contact with the teat opening all day long from faeces, soil and splashes of water. They are capable of penetrating open teat openings but usually enter the teat during milking, after being on the teat skin.

Procedures for sending in milk samples

Bacteriological testing of milk samples provides information which can be used to update the treatment plan, such as antibiotic resistance.

Sending samples in immediately

- *in cases of clinical mastitis you can send samples immediately, the results tell you if you are treating properly. The results for a period give an idea of areas for improvement. In cases of high cell counts send in samples from cows with a high cell count (CMT test indicates which quarter) and treat after the result.*

Saving up samples

Take a sample from each case of clinical mastitis. Put it in the freezer. Combine the sending in of samples from cows with high cell counts with, say, samples from newly calved cows. Options for sending in samples:

1. *monthly, before consulting the vet*
2. *monthly, after consulting the vet*
3. *annually, two weeks before discussing the farm treatment plan*
4. *when problems arise. In this situation, sampling will provide some information but stored samples may be very valuable.*

Bacteria: a reference guide

Bacterium	Characteristics	Treatment	Improving management
Streptococcus agalactiae (SAG)	Can only survive in milk so is transmitted from cow to cow with the milk. Highly contagious. Invariably subclinical infections only. Virtually eliminated in the UK, care when buying in new cattle.	Responds well to treatment with antibiotics (penicillin).	Dry off all cows with antibiotics, good milk hygiene. *(Focus: milking, treatment.)*
Staphylococcus aureus (SAU)	Highly contagious bacterium. Found on the skin of the udder and in the milk. Causes clinical and subclinical mastitis.	Results of treatment vary widely. Penicillin-sensitive strains, new infections and young cows recover reasonably well (approx. 70%). Chronic infections, older cows and multiple infections per cow have a poor recovery rate.	Identify and mark infected cows, then treat or cull. Strict measures to prevent the spread of infection. *(Focus: milking, treatment.)*
Streptococcus dysgalactiae (SDY)	Usually subclinical mastitis with very high cell count. Often infection of damaged teats (splits, injuries, badly damaged teat ends).	Usually responds well to treatment with antibiotics (penicillin).	Keep teat condition good. Dry off all cows with antibiotics. *(Focus: milking, treatment.)*
Streptococcus uberis (SUB)	Lives in the cow's surroundings (straw, cubicles, pasture, dung) and on the cow itself. Causes clinical and subclinical mastitis.	Treat clinical infections immediately in accordance with the farm treatment plan. Chronic infections have a poor chance of recovery.	Improve hygiene and dryness in cowshed and cubicles. Optimise the cow's resistance. *(Focus: milking, infection pressure, resistance.)*
Escherichia coli (ECO)	Lives in the cow's surroundings (dung, cubicles, soil). Usually causes clinical mastitis and is the major cause of toxic mastitis.	Treatment focuses on the effects of toxins, such as controlling infection and administering fluids. The bacterium often disappears from the udder quickly.	Improve hygiene and dryness in cowshed and cubicles. Optimise the cow's resistance. *(Focus: milking, resistance, infection pressure.)*
Coagulase Negative Staphylococci (STC)	A broad group of bacteria with a wide range of characteristics. Most common in early lactation of heifers, apparently rare in UK.	Preferably based on sensitivity determination. Follow farm treatment plan. Results of treatment vary widely.	Maximise heifer udder health. Optimise milking hygiene and milking technique. *(Focus: milking, resistance, treatment.)*

Targeted approach

Infections caused by contagious (milk-borne) bacteria call for better isolation of infected cows, better milking hygiene and milking technique, earlier detection (foremilk stripping/cell counts), better treatment and a contact dip. In the case of infections caused by environmental bacteria, improvements include milking hygiene in cowshed and cubicles, cow resistance and barrier dips.

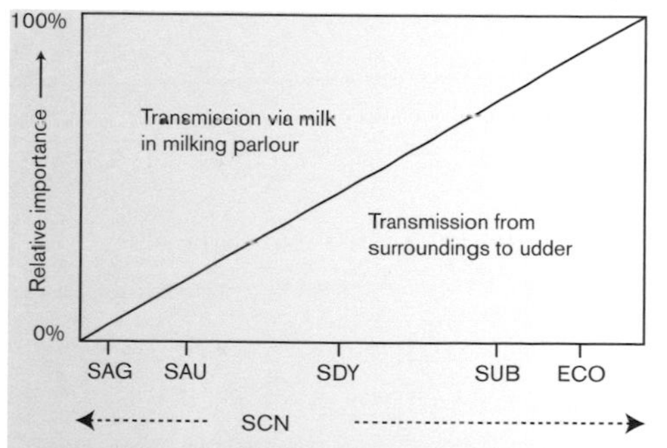

If you know which bacteria are causing your mastitis, you can target both treatment and prevention better. (R.N. Zadoks, 2002).

Laboratories use special nutrient media to identify strains of bacteria quickly. In this culture dish, the strain growing on the left is clearly different from that on the right.

Less common causes of mastitis

Nocardia

Nocardia is an environmental bacterium that lives mainly in and on the soil. May survive in certain antibiotic preparations.

Risk factors:

Working unhygienically when using intramammary tubes. Reuse of teat needles and tubes. Dirty animals.

Approach:

Cull chronic cases. If necessary, treat on basis of sensitivity determination.

Klebsiella

Klebsiella is a soil bacterium. Causes acute, severe mastitis with a sick cow. Also appears to occur fairly frequently as a subclinical infection.

Risk factors:

Damp sawdust containing tree bark. Possibly other sources as well.

Approach:

Identify the source of infection and neutralise it. Usually involves replacing sawdust in cubicles with dry sawdust.

Prothoteca

Prothoteca is an alga that is generally present in dung. Usually causes subclinical mastitis. Infections hardly ever recover. Quarters dry off slowly.

Risk factors:

Damp, warm, dung-soiled places in the cowshed.

Approach:

Identify infected cows and prevent transmission of infection. First-rate cowshed and parlour hygiene.

Yeasts

Yeasts are not bacteria and are not susceptible to antibiotics. They occur normally in the environment and on the skin of the cow. They strike after other causes have triggered mastitis (secondary infections).

Risk factors:

Working unhygienically when using intramammary tubes. Dirty animals. Reuse of teat needles and tubes.

Approach:

Cull. Improve hygiene when using intramammary tubes.

Pseudomonas

Pseudomonas is a moisture-loving environmental bacterium. Survives easily in damp, unhygienic situations. Resistant to many antibiotics. May cause very serious, fatal mastitis which is non-responsive to treatment.

Risk factors:

Unhygienic use of teat dips, injection fluid and udder cloths. Use of contaminated water during milking.

Approach:

Identify and tackle the source. Work hygienically in the milking parlour and when administering treatment. Identify and cull infected cows.

Mycoplasma

Mycoplasma is a bacterium that can infect the udder via the bloodstream. Strictly confined to cows, it may also cause joint problems and lung conditions in young stock.

Risk factors:

Buying in an infected cow, yearling, two-year-old heifer or calf. Poor milking hygiene. Feeding whole milk and mastistic milk to calves. Poor hygiene around sick cows and calves.

Approach:

Cull infected cows, or prevent all transmission of infection in the operator's pit. Identify infected cows. Don't feed mastitic milk to calves. Separate young stock and adult animals. Handle sick animals very hygienically. Don't buy in stock.

Identify in time, tackle effectively

Dairy farmers who keep accurate, up-to-date records and monitor their key data closely are quick to spot a problem developing. They then use their knowledge of nutrition, procedures and the causes of mastitis to take effective action, so as to minimise losses and preserve the working rhythm of the farm. The next four pages explain how to detect and tackle problems. There is no one right approach, a number of different strategies are outlined.

Success or failure

The outcome of the approach taken to a problem is determined in every case by two factors:

1. the certainty with which the causes of the problems are established; you need a correct diagnosis if you are to tackle the right target. If you know the cause, the solution is usually clear.
2. the accuracy and determination with which you carry out the improvements on the farm. Be open to change and make sure you understand why and how you have to change. Get your advisor to help you carry out the improvements. Consult him/her if you have any doubts or encounter problems.

Problem 1: More than 10% new alerts

If the number of new cows with an alert approaches or exceeds 10%, the cell count will soar. This is your cue to take immediate action. The number of new alerts is therefore the first indicator as to whether your udder health is under control. An alert = a new case of a high cell count: 1st parity cow ≥150.000, 2+ parity ≥250.000.

The first thing you need to do is prevent new infections, which involves trying to cure the cows with a high cell count. What do you know and what should you do?

1. **You have bacteriological test results and four-weekly cow cell count data.** *The nature of the organisms gives a good idea of where the problem lies. If they are contagious bacteria, focus your attention on milking and treatment. If they are environmental bacteria, concentrate first on the infection pressure from the surroundings and resistance (of cow and udder). With your vet, carry out a thorough analysis and draw up an improvement plan. Adapt the farm treatment plan if necessary.*
2. **You don't know which bacteria are causing most infections and don't have reliable cow cell count data. Start collecting these immediately.** *In the mean time you have to take general measures and have to guess. With your vet, go through all five areas of the five-point plan. This may highlight major problems in one area or, equally, a need for improvements in all five areas. Have a dynamic milking assessment carried out. Draw up a plan for identifying infected cows immediately and treating them appropriately.*

Problem 2: Too much clinical mastitis

This step-by-step plan is structured to move from identifying the problem, through identifying the cause, to targeted intervention. If you carry out measures without properly identifying the cause, they may result in an improvement, but you won't know why or what worked, so you won't be in control.

Step 1: Unravelling the situation	Step 2: Identify and tackle the problem		Step 3: Carry out structural improvements
≥ 10% cows have cell count > 250,000	*Yes: Clinical mastitis is largely the result of the high cell count.*		
Tank cell count >250,00	*Yes: Follow the approach for high cell count problems.*		
≥ 25% of the high cell count cows had clinical mastitis earlier in lactation	*Yes: Carry out bacteriological testing of mastitis cases*	*SDY in particular:* *– implement treatment plan better.*	*Treatment* *Monitoring*
		SUB in particular: *– improve treatment and/or cull earlier;* *– reduce infection pressure from lying areas.*	*Treatment* *Infection pressure* *Monitoring*
		ECO in particular: *– determine farm-specific approach.*	*Resistance* *Infection pressure from surroundings* *Monitoring*
		Other causes *– determine farm-specific approach.*	*Determine farm-specific approach*
< 25% of the high cell count cows had clinical mastitis earlier in lactation	*Yes: Carry out bacteriological testing of mastitis cases*	*SDY in particular:* *– implement treatment plan better, improve dry cow therapy.*	*Milking* *Treatment, Resistance*
		SUB in particular: *– reduce infection pressure from lying areas.*	*Milking* *Infection pressure, Resistance*
		ECO in particular: *– improve nutrition and management in dry period and early lactation;* *– reduce infection pressure from the surroundings in transition period;* *– optimise milking machine/milking technique.*	*Resistance* *Infection pressure from surroundings* *Milking*
		Other causes *– determine farm-specific approach*	*Determine farm-specific approach*
Also assess risk groups and risk periods:			
Mainly heifers	*Follow approach for heifer mastitis.*		
Mainly in the winter *Mainly in the summer*	*Monitor infection pressure, ventilation, climate (including heat stress), cow comfort and nutrition.*		*Infection pressure* *Resistance*
Mainly newly calved cows	*Monitor dry period management and treatment, milking machine and milking technique, hygiene around calving, nutrition in transition period.*		*Resistance* *Milking* *Treatment* *Infection pressure*

This schedule illustrates the lines along which an expert might think and act during a consultation.

Problems and how to tackle them

Problem 3: Too much clinical mastitis in heifers

Take action if there is more than one case of clinical mastitis to every ten heifers in the first month after calving.

Controll points:

1. monitor and improve resistance of the heifers	***Action points:***
– *vitamins/minerals (vitamin E, Se, Cu and Mg)*	*tests blood, urine, liver biopsy*
– *stress (introduction procedure)*	*advisor: assesses procedure, nutrition, animals*
– *diet and feed intake (udder oedema, colostrum production and calcium)*	*feed advisor: carries out complete analysis*
– *calving (stress and hygiene)*	*assesses advisor: procedure, situation, animals*
– *health (hooves, BVD, etc.)*	*assesses advisor: animals and data*

2. REDUCE INFECTION PRESSURE:

– *lying area hygiene*	*clean twice a day, heifers not with milking cows, calving pen perfectly clean and dry*
– *teat end hygiene*	*daily dipping before calving*
– *treat infections*	*farm treatment plan*

Forty percent of clinical mastitis cases in heifers occur in the first month after calving. Reduced resistance of the heifer and her udder mean that the animal is unable to fight off mild infections and succumbs to mastitis.

Problem 4: A high tank cell count (over 250,000)

Breaking down the problem:		***Tests and investigations:***	***Improvements:***	***Cause of the problem:***
Does less than 10% of the herd have a cell count below 250,000? (No ↓)	*Yes* →	*You have a number of problem cows:* *– carry out bacteriological testing on all high cell count cows.*	*– decide on the best treatment for each cow, or cull.*	*You are treating high cell count cows too late and/or not treating them properly.* *Cull chronic cases earlier.*
Are there fewer than 10% new alerts? (cell count over 250,000) (No ↓)	*Yes* →	*You have a lot of chronic infections:* *– determine if there are any risk groups or risk periods;* *– carry out bacteriological testing on all high cell count cows.*	*– improve resistance and/or reduce infection pressure in the risk groups and risk periods;* *– use the bacteriological test results and sensitivity determination to improve the farm treatment plan.*	*Infections are not recovering well. This may be due to reduced resistance in certain risk cows, or during certain periods.* *It may also be because the treatment administered is inadequate, or the bacteria are highly resistant.*
→		*You have a lot of new infections:* *– have your milking machine and milking machine assessed;* *– do you have more than 15% repeat cases?* *– monitor the cows' resistance.*	*– improve the milking machine, your milking technique and teat dipping;* *– improve your treatments and cull cows earlier;* *– tackle factors that reduce resistance.*	*New infections are constantly emerging, or old infections flaring up. Most infections occur during milking. Reduced herd resistance may be the weakest link.*

Important notes:
1. In every case, a particular mastitis bacterium may be the cause of the problem. This can be determined only with bacteriological testing. Before tackling the problem, an expert will have to determine farm-specific measures.
2. It normally takes a prolonged period of increased attentiveness and effort to solve a problem once and for all. Usually, what is needed is for you and/or your staff to make a permanent change in your way of working.
3. The situation in practice may be different from, or more complicated than this schedule: check with your vet.

Problems and how to tackle them

Cow signals indicating areas for improvement in milking:

1. Poor entry to milking parlour

Possible causes:

1. *difficult entrance (too narrow, steps, tight turns, lack of visibility);*
2. *slippery floor;*
3. *confined space;*
4. *milking machine causing pain;*
5. *no moving barrier/no fresh feed after visiting the parlour (parlours without concentrates);*
6. *farmer's attitude to cows in the parlour;*
7. *poor cow flow.*

2. Soiled udders

Possible causes:

1. *not enough bedding in cubicles;*
2. *damp bedding (over-stocking, lack of bedding, poor ventilation);*
3. *cubicle dimensions wrong;*
4. *too much milk leakage;*
5. *watery dung (nutrition);*
6. *cows lying in passage way;*
7. *not enough cubicles;*
8. *over-stocked straw yards.*

3. Cow not letting milk down

Possible causes:

1. *inadequate pre-treatment;*
2. *no waiting time after pre-treatment;*
3. *cow anxious / sick / on heat / in pain;*
4. *milking machine not set properly.*

4. Clusters suck in air during milking

Possible causes:

1. *weight of cluster distributed incorrectly (tube guides);*
2. *wrong teat liners;*
3. *insufficient vacuum;*
4. *insufficient milk removal capacity;*
5. *agitated cows.*

5. Cows agitated during milking

Possible causes:

1. *Milking machine not working properly*
   Cow signals:
   - *I. especially towards end of milking;*
   - *II. teats painful after milking;*
   - *III. possibly poor teat condition.*
2. *Seeking concentrates*
   Cow signals:
   - *I. udder not painful;*
   - *II. starts when feed is almost finished.*
3. *Flies*
   Cow signals:
   - *I. presence of flies swishes tail;*
   - *II. also agitated before and after milking.*
4. *Milking place too cramped*
   Cow signals:
   - *I. cows entering the stall poorly;*
   - *II. cows standing crooked in the stall;*
   - *III. affects the largest animals in particular.*
5. *Sensitive teats*
   Cow signals:
   - *I. trodden teats;*
   - *II. blisters;*
   - *III. udder inflammation;*
   - *IV. chapped teats (see teat condition);*
   - *V. chemicals (foot baths, lime, disinfectants).*
6. *Agitation on part of milker*
   Cow signals:
   - *I. cows afraid of the milker.*
7. *Poor cow flow*
   Cow signals:
   - *I. suddenly kick off the cluster;*
   - *II. poor milking out/fluctuating milk production;*
   - *III. cows trip;*
   - *IV. time can vary widely;*
   - *V. cows enter the milking parlour poorly.*

In comparison with a parallel parlor, a herringbone parlor offers a better view on the udder, better positioning of the cluster, and more ergononomic working.

6. Poor condition of teat skin and teat end hyperkeratosis

Possible causes:

1. *stiff/tight teat liner;*
2. *milking speed too low;*
3. *vacuum too high;*
4. *detaching cluster too late;*
5. *weather influences (sunburn, changeable weather);*
6. *chemicals (foot baths, lime, cleaning agents and disinfectants).*

Problem 5: Problems with the udder skin

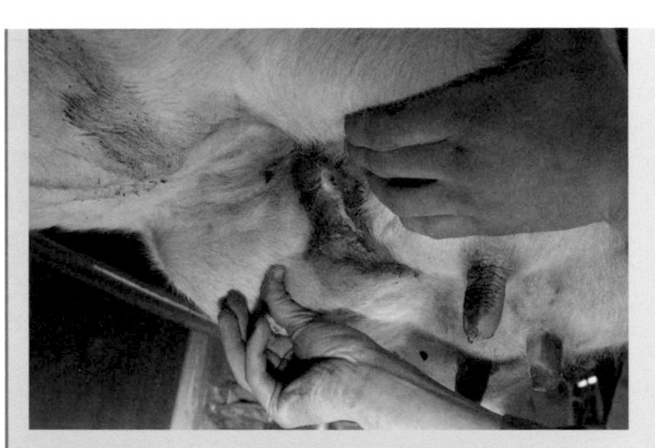

Udder eczema. A similar infection may be present between the udder and hind leg. As yet, little is known about its cause or treatment. Probably due to moisture and poor circulation, usually in early lactation. The agents responsible are skin bacteria and fungal infections. Treatment consists of disinfectant emollient salves.

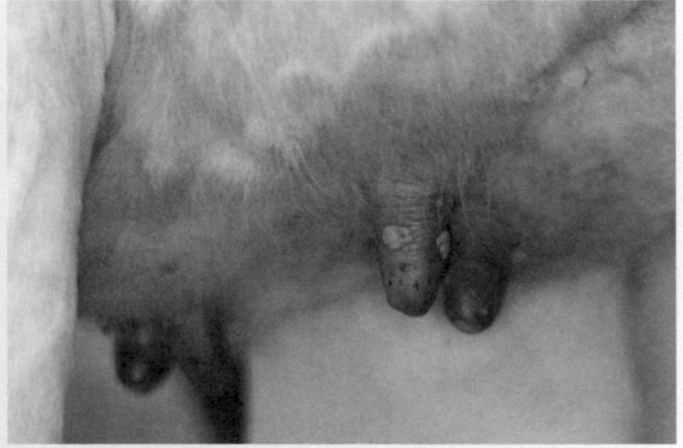

Warts are caused by viruses. There are many viruses and many types of wart. Problematic if they are in or around the teat opening or are painful. Good milking hygiene can prevent transmission (effectivedisinfectant dip, a clean cloth for every udder).

Arcanobacter pyogenes causes summer mastitis and is a risk where there are damaged teats. Sources of infection include flies and the cubicle floor. Infected quarters secrete pus and are beyond saving. Treat the animal with antibiotics if it is sick and in order to nip the infection in the bud.

Bacterial infection of a patch of udder eczema, probably due to S. aureus. S. aureus is a skin bacterium that may cause a range of inflammations and wound infections. People can carry strains of S. aureus on their hands, which can cause mastitis.

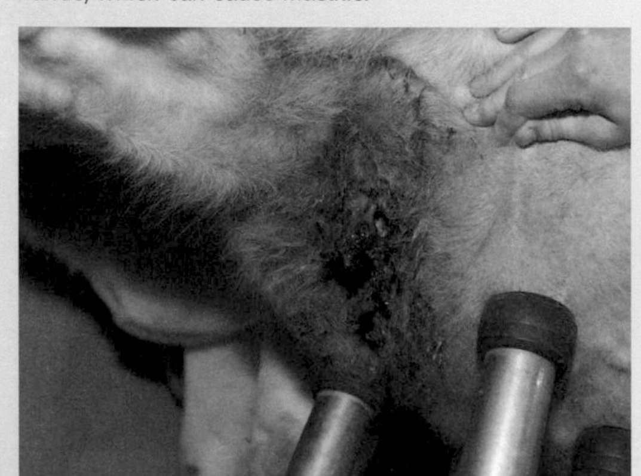

Pseudo-cowpox virus causes blisters that quickly burst. The resulting pain makes cows very difficult to milk. Use analgesic sprays during milking and wound salve afterwards. The problem resolves by itself. An effective teat dip kills the virus. Consult your vet.

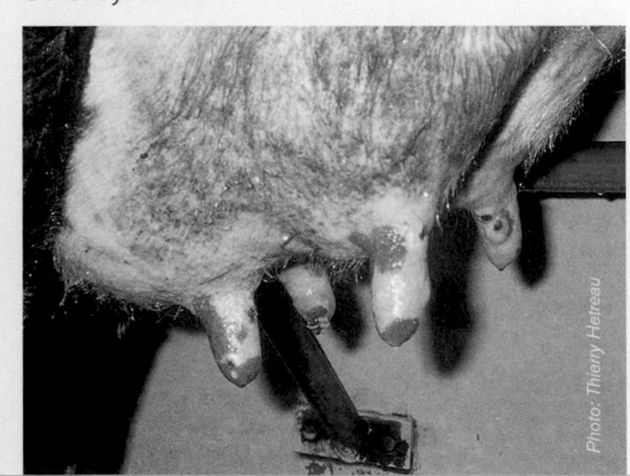

Photo: Thierry Hetreau

Necrotic (dying) teat in a heifer. Sometimes parts of the teat skin die off. Occurs around calving, usually in a single animal. Consult your vet if you have more than one case. The exact cause is unknown. Poor circulation plays a role. Check selenium intake.

Problem 6: UNOs: Unclassified notable observations

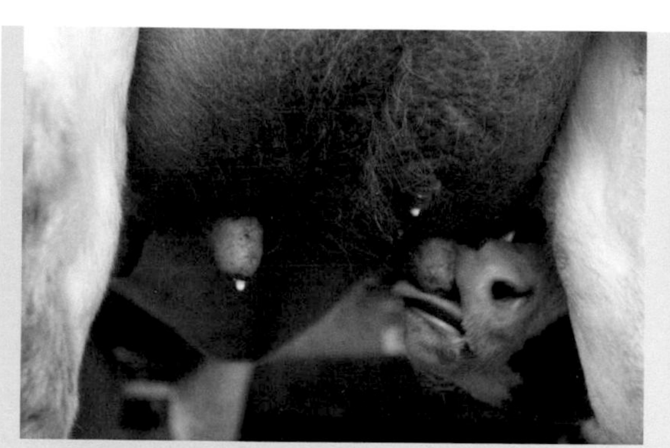

Accessory teats have their own "quarter" and produce milk after calving. The calf's suckling triggers the release of oxytocin and the cow lets down milk. If you don't milk it, the accessory teat will dry off. Accessory teats can also get mastitis.

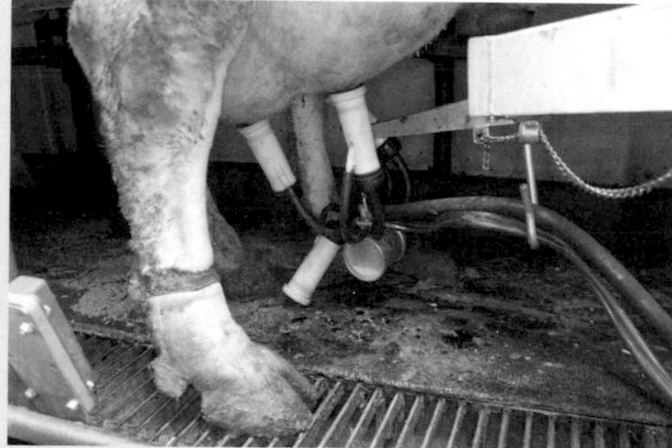

If a cow has three teats, it is difficult to distribute the weight of the cluster evenly between the teats. Milk a three-teater with a cap over the unused teat cup and suspend the cluster in the correct position under the udder. Make sure you have clean caps within reach.

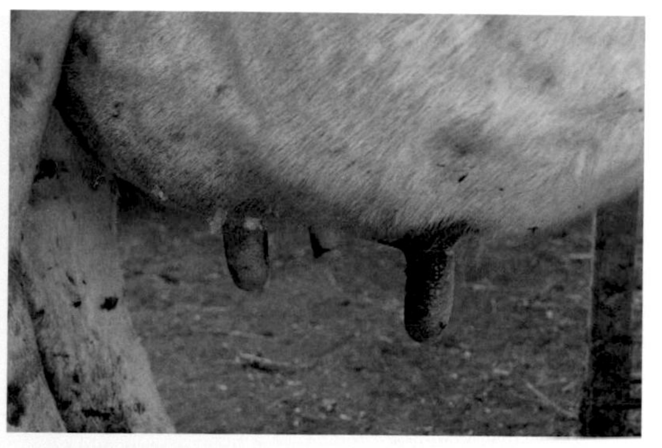

Sunburn. Very painful, causes the cow to milk out badly. Often combined with heat stress. The combination increases the risk of mastitis. Make sure there is shade in the pasture, or keep cows indoors during the day. Treat with emollient salve. Apply sunscreen (factor 20) to cows at risk.

Accessory teats can get in the way during milking. Your vet can remove troublesome accessory teats during the dry period.

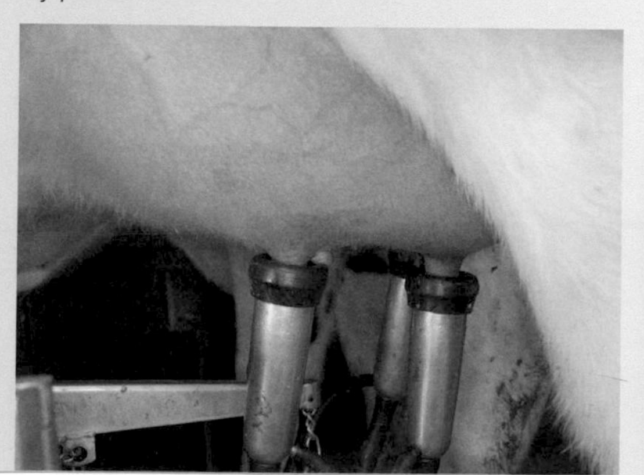

In side-by-side stalls, cows have to make very tight turns. Cows have trouble with this movement, which puts a heavy stress on their hooves. If the cow is calm or on a soft surface, it will be OK. But if the cow is hurried along and/or the floor is very uneven, the result is sole ulcer defects and a stressed cow.

Dung on a cow's hind quarters is almost always from the cow itself. It indicates that its dung is or has been too watery.
Watery dung is the result of problems with nutrition or feed intake, or illness. It is invariably accompanied by reduced resistance.

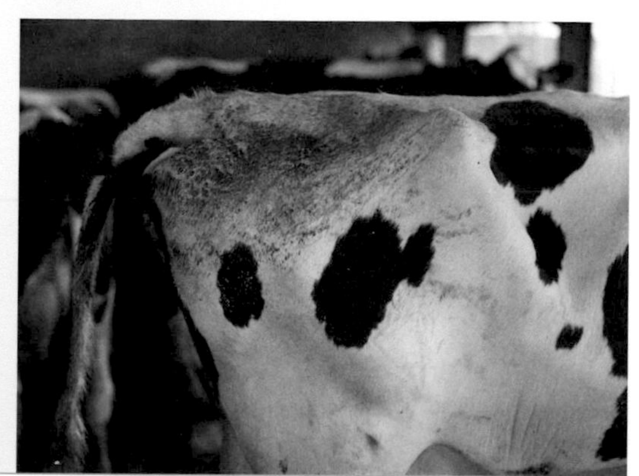

Index